"This neural lens gives me a totally different approach to my way of teaching. Our Hopi students need this way of thinking, and I plan to pass along what I've learned to my administrator and to other educators here in Arizona."
            —*April Honahnie*, K-8 Teacher
            at Hotevilla-Bacavi Community School, AZ

"Finally, the science behind what works in learning! This is training unlike all other professional learning because it is continuously rooted in the 'why'. This work explains how the brain interacts with environmental and internal stimuli with the overarching goal of supporting each teacher's understanding of enough neuroscience to shift daily learning."
            —*Rosa M. Villarreal*, Principal of Kent Elementary School, WA

"This is crusader work. Dr. O'Mahony is rowing against the current, but this important book will stand the test of time."
            —*Terry Bergeson*, Washington State Superintendent of Public Instruction (former) and Interim Dean (retired) of the School of Education and Kinesiology at Pacific Lutheran University, USA

"This book will be important for every teacher because knowledge is power. I am shocked and delighted to learn things about the brain that are so valuable in my daily classroom practice, especially in distance learning spaces. Amygdala, hippocampus, and working memory mean so much more to me now. This is the future of human enhancement!"
            —*Stéphanie Turcotte*, Teacher
            at École Claudette-et-Denis-Tardif, Canada

"Learning about children's thinking from the inside out has given me a new perspective on education as a teacher. I now see students, and my own children, through what is going on inside their minds and their thinking rather than feeling frustrated that they are not doing things exactly the way that I have told them to. Knowing your 'orchid students' and teaching with them in mind will yield greater results than driving on without them and then trying to formulate interventions to catch them up."
            —*Sean Sturgill*, Fifth Grade Teacher
            at Lackamas Elementary, Yelm Community Schools, WA

The Brain-Based Classroom

The Brain-Based Classroom translates findings from educational neuroscience into a new paradigm of practices suitable for any teacher. The human brain is a site of spectacular capacity for joy, motivation, and personal satisfaction, but how can educators harness its potential to help children reach truly fulfilling goals? Using this innovative collection of brain-centric strategies, teachers can transform their classrooms into deep learning spaces that support their students through self-regulation and mindset shifts. These fresh insights will help teachers resolve classroom management issues, prevent crises and disruptive behaviors, and center social-emotional learning and restorative practices.

Kieran O'Mahony is Founding Principal of the Institute for Connecting Neuroscience with Teaching and Learning, USA, and Founder and Chairman of the Board of Neural Education.

The Brain-Based Classroom

Accessing Every Child's Potential Through Educational Neuroscience

Kieran O'Mahony

Routledge
Taylor & Francis Group

NEW YORK AND LONDON

First published 2021
by Routledge
52 Vanderbilt Avenue, New York, NY 10017

and by Routledge
2 Park Square, Milton Park, Abingdon, Oxon, OX14 4RN

Routledge is an imprint of the Taylor & Francis Group, an informa business

Library of Congress Cataloging-in-Publication Data
A catalog record for this title has been requested

ISBN: 978-0-367-61709-7 (hbk)
ISBN: 978-0-367-61011-1 (pbk)
ISBN: 978-1-003-10615-9 (ebk)

Typeset in Palatino
by Apex CoVantage, LLC

Dedication

To neural educators—the pedagogy of tomorrow, today

Contents

Figures

Acknowledgments

This book would not have happened without a great deal of help and support, and I'm happy to have the chance to say thank you. Teachers are primary, because educational neuroscience carries the promise of accessing every child's potential.

I'm indebted to learning scientists and neuroscientists who shared work and ideas with me. In particular, I'm grateful to scholars and research scientists who collaborated on NSF and NIH projects. I am honored to have received insights into particular aspects of the learning sciences from colleagues at LIFE and NIDA, at iLABS, SRI, and Stanford College of Education, and at CELEST, SILC, and RAPID.

I am especially grateful to the dozens of students, teachers, and parents who graciously shared their classroom experiences. The stories are all true, but in some cases, names and settings have been changed to protect identities.

A number of people generously read and improved chapters of the manuscript. Special thanks to Missy Widmann and neural education champions who are changing the landscape of teaching every day. Thanks to Esther Mose, Ashley Valentine, Rich Carr, and Tom Lee.

I would never have started the book without the encouragement of Michael Bledsoe, a visionary sage. I am grateful for the napkin sketch that charted an outline—artist Michael Peck. I thank my publisher, Daniel Schwartz, for his attentive guidance.

Most important, I'd like to thank my children, who inspired me to become a better parent and teacher. Thank you to Shane, Ronan, Madelein, and Noel-Finn. They are part and parcel of everything I do with learning and brain.

Special thanks to J. K. and to J. B.

Preface

Teaching with brain should be a no-brainer. Yet, very few of us know enough fundamentals of how the human brain works or, for that matter, are familiar enough with the delicate dance that is the intersection of neuroscience and pedagogy to be successful at teaching with the brain. It is this conundrum that **Neural Education** seeks to address.

The body of knowledge with practice that is contained in this book emerged from design research projects in learning theory and implementation. Several fields of research emerged separately but came to a critical confluence at the end of the decade of the brain (1990–2000). This coincided with **LIFE** (Learning in Informal and Formal Environments), first National Science Foundation (NSF) Science of Learning Center (SLC). LIFE members were awarded $50 million over ten years to study how children learn. On the heels of this center, a cross-disciplinary research project sponsored by the **National Institutes for Health** (1) merged learning models with neural substrates to learning theory and thus advanced the field further. Over time, this research collaboration refined itself into a method and a process. From these various origins, a method of neuroscience and learning science blended into a pedagogy that had real potential for teachers.

As teachers quickly embraced a neural solution, it became clear that this effort consisted of three separate but intertwined elements to form a rickety three-legged stool (teacher, student, and guardian). If one leg was wobbly, the center fell out—the structure lost its stability. Neural Education worked best when all three legs stand solid on the ground. The neuroscience of learning was needed in classrooms where both teachers and students were given rudimentary and life-changing information about how the human brain works and how children learn.

The cognitive three Rs make up a critical aspect of Neural Education—Reflect, Revised Thinking, and Report Out. *Reflection* is a personalized method that fosters agentic, metacognitive processes. In reflection, we are empowered to take charge of our own learning in a way that makes us feel good, purposeful, and with an informed mindset. It requires a careful scaffolding methodology that is inherent in a Neural Education paradigm. *Revised Thinking* delivers a personal voyage of cognitive rehearsal throughout these pages so that it is possible to see one's thinking shift, to make new neural connections, and to live in the learning. *Report Out* is personalized to the reader's domain of practice.

The Neural Education premise is that you find a pedagogic model that works for you no matter if it is face-to-face, blended, or remote. A lens that is informed by the human brain's capacity for learning and self-realization will ensure success.

About the Author

Dr. Kieran O'Mahony is Founder of the Institute for Connecting Neuroscience with Teaching and Learning. As a learning scientist with a focus on cognitive neuroscience, he participated in groundbreaking research at the University of Washington's College of Education and the LIFE Center, the first NSF-funded Science of Learning Center in the study of the social aspects of learning and how children learn. His work is substantively applicable for teachers in their pedagogy, their classroom management, and their social and emotional stance in diverse learning spaces.

At the Institute, Dr. O'Mahony and his team have pioneered a new approach to professional development through Neural Education, a program designed for all child caregivers. These include general and special education teachers, paraeducators, occupational therapists, school psychologists, teachers of English language learners, bus drivers, cafeteria workers, front office staff, custodians—anybody who serves children as they engage with their world of learning. Neural Education has reinvented teachers' understanding of pedagogy and classroom management by reframing their practice with foundational constructs of neuroscience that enable comfortable brain-based classroom experiences, both face-to-face and online. The program's fast-growing groundswell of active Neural Educators meet in monthly professional learning communities to share and grow their knowledge of and experiences in child learning and brain-based classrooms.

As a winner of the prestigious Phi Beta Kappa Pathfinder Award for his pioneering efforts on behalf of child learning in brain-based classrooms, Dr. O'Mahony is acknowledged as a key pedagogy influencer who "encourages others to seek new worlds to discover, pathways to explore, and untouched destinations to reach." As new knowledge and discoveries are made at the bio-molecular level in brain labs, and as research results emerge from modern scanning devices (e.g., FMRI, DTI), Dr. O'Mahony leads Neural Education experts in translating these findings into practices and processes that transform teaching and learning. Together with teachers who are immersed in a neural lens, Neural Educators co-create methods and models that impact teaching and learning in schools, workplaces, and homes.

Introduction

Two questions drive this book. Though situated in any 21st century classroom, each question derives from a pair of unrelated but landmark events that were set in motion in the middle of the last century. The first question emanates from a noteworthy meeting of the Special Interest Group on Information Theory that took place at MIT on September 11, 1956. All teachers live under the shadow of what happened in that room on that day. The second question is focused on a paradigm shift that distinguishes behaviorist beginnings from mentalistic models related to neuroscience and learning. Both questions have implications for engagement and safety in learning spaces. These are the questions that teachers might ask themselves:

- ◆ What would I do differently if I used a cognitive neural lens in my classroom?
- ◆ How can I affect cognitive change in a behaviorist system?

Though we situate the questions in k12 learning spaces, they are equally meaningful for learning spaces in any workplace.

The neural lens is critical. Our brains are what make us who we are. They are the seat of personal identity and autonomy. Our biological system is made up of billions of neurons communicating with one another. It also includes chemicals in the blood as well as bacteria in the gut. We recognize a "gut" feeling for a person, place, or thing that sometimes makes all the difference. We are creatures of interaction and reaction. Genetics and epigenetics play their part, too. Our being is affected by where we were born, guardians who raised us, schools we attended, and social contexts in which we grow up.

Every day, in schools and homes, we see the results of genetics and environment at play. Children either thrive or struggle to learn. Guardians anguish over why one of their amazing children cannot compete in academics, or contribute at sports, and will show up in a negative and reactive way against all expectations and wishes. At the same time, we witness children who used to be dysregulated, disruptive, aggressive, and troubled achieve personal successes in the face of insurmountable odds that ought to incapacitate even the most resilient of our species. What is the difference? How can we explain the connection between the brain, personality, identity, and potential?

In this book, we attempt to draw together strings of neuroscience and learning sciences in order to make sense of children in their social contexts. It comes as a relief to teachers and guardians to know that there is a solution to the many distracting and disruptive behaviors that seem to dominate optimal learning scenarios. We explain, first, the neuronal structures that underlie learning. We accompany these with appropriate pedagogic nuances to illuminate successful learning environments. All children are born to learn; they are hardwired learning-machines. Yet, it is not a given that all children will achieve success even with purposeful mediation and practice. Knowledgeable and well-meaning guardians and teachers can lose some children.

Teachers are, therefore, the most important focus of this book. While we are interested in knowing about our brains and questions relating to personality, identity, and consciousness, we focus our inquiry in areas that pertain mostly to the learning brain. For instance, how does this piece of information about the hippocampus or amygdala relate to a child in a classroom? At the same time, we want to help guardians understand their child in the home. We view every piece of information through a lens that asks the question— does this information help a teacher who is doing her best to manage a disruptive student?

Sometimes that student is simply following the brain's imperative, which is to survive. After all, our species—Homo sapiens—made it to this time and place! We are the ultimate survivors. As social beings, we appear to have an uncanny ability to "accurately" assess danger and the intelligence of another person. Such evolutionary preparedness for survival remains with every child in everyday social interactions. It's a complex space. To reach into a child's learning world, we might encounter conscious effort or subconscious involuntary reactivity, social capacity that is contributive or combative for engagement, and emotional intelligence that fosters or hinders growth.

Each brain is unique. Consciousness is unique to each individual. Mind, brain, and consciousness are in play for each individual separately. Mind is a person's intellect—that something that enables one to be aware of their world. It allows us to engage with experiences, especially to think, and to feel. Mind is, thus, the faculty of consciousness and thought. The various functions of mind, like rationalizing and learning, are a set of processes carried out by the brain. Mind capacities are referred to as cognitive ability.

The word "cognitive" conjures a rich envelope for concepts that include notions of reasoning, predicting, and thinking. Without the brain, the mind would not function. For instance, stroke victims typically experience difficulty engaging in normal mental functions. Short-term memory exhibits degrees of impairment. Sometimes, they experience disorientation and have difficulties partaking in easy conversations. It is because we are able to think, feel, argue, laugh, act, learn, remember, and create that we are who we are. The brain is only roughly three pounds of squishy vesicles, yet it produces our every emotional and intellectual act. It determines our moods. It is also immensely powerful and full of potential—it can endow us with the capability for great joy, terrible fears, real sadness, and awful misery.

Teachers often struggle with disruptive and aggressive children. It seems that, for a lot of learners, anxiety can trigger a fight, flight, freeze reaction to "normal" teaching scenarios. The involuntary reactive system is triggered in situations of looming threat or imminent danger. For instance, in the wild, a baby zebra might react in a flight scenario when a lion chases it. Why is it that some children can manage to stay engaged, pay attention, follow instructions, and generally do well when the teacher introduces a new challenge, but other children become aggressive, disruptive, even antisocial? Disruptive individuals take everyone else down with them. It's a lose-lose situation.

Teachers and guardians who are informed about how the human brain works and how children learn are quick to recognize when a child reaches the limitations of working memory. Too much information (typically at a time when the brain is already in an amygdala hijack) means learners are unable to process. What is working memory? What are its limitations? And what is amygdala hijack? The neural lens that this book will uncover focuses on understanding and demystifying these items.

Too often, teacher focus is on content. So much to teach and so little time! Such constraints are immediate triggers for cognitive overload. A perfect storm of inattention, frustration, fear, and anxiety manifests into amygdala hijack, with its constituent disruptive behaviors, acting out with aggression. Teachers' ability to recognize, manage, and defuse an amygdala hijack is probably the most valuable toolkit that a neural lens delivers.

Working memory is not something that teachers typically strategize for as they prepare their lesson plans. Yet, it is often the most critical constraint that hampers a child's ability to stay focused, to pay attention, to engage with fellows and/or content, and to feel good about progress. Teachers always ask, "Are there any techniques for increasing a child's working memory?" The welcoming answer is a rousing YES! We can be intentional about increasing a child's working memory, so that by the end of even one week, perceptible improvement can be obtained. Unfortunately, most everything the teacher does or says has the capacity to also decrease this hardwired biological phenomenon. It's not the first thought that comes into a teacher's head—"am I impacting the child's working memory?"

These important pedagogic considerations do matter if we are to improve learning. School can be stressful for children. Adults should not make it more stressful by not knowing the critical components about what working memory is and how to engage with it. Teachers who are familiar with the neuroscience of learning are fully aware of the brain's processing limitations and, in addition, cognizant of the many techniques for helping children navigate this difficult space. Children are born with the potential to learn, but they are not always able to get there on their own.

The learning brain is the focus of this book. Learning is about neuronal communication. Connection occurs through interacting circuitry in an electro-chemical exchange of information. Action potentials result in electrical propagation along axons, which, in turn, excite chemical exchanges at the synapse. A synapse is a space between two neurons—between the terminal of neuron one and the dendrites of neuron two. At the axon terminal, presynaptic vesicles are prompted to release chemical messengers (neurotransmitters) into the synaptic cleft, where dendrites from the next neuron are looking to bind with them. Postsynaptic receptors on these dendrites scoop up appropriate neurotransmitters and, depending on whether the message is excitatory or inhibitory, decides what to do with it. Since communication occurs at the synapse, it is easy to see that the synapse is currency for learning.

We highlight structural building blocks of the brain's capacity for communication. The definition of learning is grounded in the physicality of making connections. To get there, it is necessary to comprehend mental models that uncover components, interconnections, and circuitry. Learning is a complex act involving survival, emotions, and logic. The brain is a busy and complex entity. Thus, learning is an intensely personal survival dance with partners like interest, attention, and working memory and, meanwhile, the brain is always learning something. We might think we know how to create optimal learning spaces, but what works for one child might be the exact opposite for the next child. When teacher says $X+Y=Z$, we have no idea how each child will interpret it. We can point out supporting methods and strategies, but acknowledge that there are as many covert as overt curricular items that embellish and/or hinder learning.

For this reason, the book is provisioned in functional sections that speak to the complexity of the learning process and to ongoing demands on various actors and inter-actors that contribute to success. We outline three grand schemas that propel the book's forward motion: *Breaking Paradigms*, *Rethinking Pedagogy*, and *Conceptual Collisions*. We ask questions in each chapter. We offer evidence for why certain methods and practices work. Some are heady constructs. Neuroscientists are quick to admit that we have but a delicate toehold in this new world of circuitry and chemistry, of synaptic currency, and inhibition. It's an exciting gateway into the world of cognition.

In **Part I,** we explore methodologies for engagement with increased capacity for learning. Chapter 1 sets up neural substrates for learning and the lens through which teachers view their world. Chapter 2 looks at the pervasive methodology that is steeped in grades, stars, and positive stimuli in order to cajole, coerce, or otherwise cause the child to enact behavior that is deemed appropriate and acceptable. Chapter 3 explicates why we revert back to Affect instead of Effect in the modern classroom. Chapter 4 examines the outcomes of children that are coerced, cajoled, or otherwise caused to desist from enacting behaviors that are deemed inappropriate or unacceptable. Chapter 5 focuses on underlying neural science that highlights the importance of physical activity, especially crossing the midline to foster powerful learning practice. Chapter 6 focuses on an intentional shift from a behaviorist rewards and punishment, to a teaching and learning model that is informed by a carefully curated neural perspective. Chapter 7 focuses on identifying and teaching to the most highly sensitive children as a way that engages and ignites optimal learning.

In **Part II,** we highlight neural constructs that are fundamental to original thinking. Chapter 8 unearths a paper from 1956 that changed the world, but seems to have been undiscovered by teachers. Chapter 9 rediscovers the man who gave us the notion of neural circuitry and systems. Chapter 10 dives deep into how the learning world shifts if we truly understand a malleable brain. Chapter 11 reveals science's most attractive cellular model for learning and memory. Chapter 12 reveals a hidden feature of the survival brain that wields a powerful impact on the learning brain. Chapter 13 illuminates groundbreaking work, which looks at the construct of fixedness in relation to intelligence and talent. Chapter 14 outlines seminal work related to learning for adaptive or routine expertise.

In **Part III,** we reveal strategies that are essential for 21st century skills. Chapter 15 reveals a powerful new way to motivate children so that they can excel by being prepared for future learning. Chapter 16 illustrates an affective method for nurturing learning environments for safety. Chapter 17 engages inextricably with a need for autonomy as a child locates identity. Chapter 18 defines the cognitive revolution and places it firmly in the realm of learning. Chapter 19 asks the question, "What if Maslow didn't take into account the sensitivity of Orchid Children?" Chapter 20 tackles a difficult episode in education that confounded progress. Chapter 21 unearths a critical flaw in

Thorndikian educational thinking—one that had profound impact in teaching systems for many generations.

The book ends with an **Epilogue** that attempts to bring neuroscience together with methods and practice for success. Research evidence and empirical data is provided in the references, glossary, and index.

Today's learning space inhabits a very unique era for children, their guardians, and teachers. For the first time ever, we have access to information that illuminates what is really happening at this developmental age inside individuals' heads. This is the first generation that has access to this kind of information.

Part I
Breaking Paradigms

1

Neuroscience of Learning

I feel so helpless . . . I don't know what to do! It's my daughter. I am at my wit's end.

—*Guardian*

Teachers are not easily convinced. They have witnessed so many attempts to increase student academic performance that they are wary of the next change *du jour*. "If you KNEW the kind of students that I deal with, you would never suggest anything so crazy. Fifty bouncing balls in my classroom will be pure chaos, broken windows, fighting, and . . . and mayhem." Then, a week later, they beat down my door. "Why didn't you tell me sooner? How come I never knew this stuff?" What happens in the meantime is not a miracle . . . it is simply science. And when something works, and works every time, teachers are quick to want more. That has been my experience over the past ten years, since Neural Education gained a limpid toehold in classrooms in a practical way.

In the beginning, I would have said the same thing . . . agreeing with naysayers, that it would be foolhardy to introduce more distractions, foolish to invite chaos where there was a tenuous, if intermittent, calm. Yet, today I never start a lesson without first inviting the entire class to engage in a physical exercise designed to improve learning. The idea is threefold: free up working memory; increase blood flow to the brain; and fill the room with appropriate neurotransmitters for learning. Appropriate neurotransmitters include dopamine, serotonin, norepinephrine, and oxytocin. That means children are out of their seats, moving kinesthetically in a structured way that is both fun and challenging. It is part of every classroom norm, so children expect it. In fact, if I do not do it right, or if I am late in starting, the children remind me. They expect a safe, fun, and energetic start to every lesson.

Paradigm Shift

For me, that is a paradigm shift from the way in which I managed my classroom in the past. I was a strict disciplinarian because I wanted to give my students a sense of responsibility and a level of consequences for their behavior—good and bad. I was convinced that I was doing them a favor. I thought I was setting them up for life. After all, the school had standards by which it gained its reputation for success, and its ethos/culture for improving children's academic outcomes. In colorful introductory brochures, we claimed that we used emergent ideations to better the lives of our students; that we knew what we were doing so that your children would excel in life. I bought into this positive marketing language because I joined the profession that I loved in order to make a difference for young children. The next generation was going to be better than their parents' generation. They would have more opportunity, would do well in life, love, and work.

So what happened?

In retrospect, it was a no brainer! I should have seen it sooner. Why would a ten-year-old child say the words "I hate school" and viscerally mean it? It just doesn't make sense. All guardians recognize this dismal attitude towards learning in organized learning. The two-year-old had become a belligerent pre-teen. For a moment, she was insatiable, simply couldn't get enough knowledge, and was forever asking "why" and "what" questions. Why would that same eager child grow to hate the sacred place of learning within just a few years?

All children have brains—hardwired learning machines (see Figure 1.1). Right from the get-go, every child is a veritable vacuum sucking up as much knowledge and skills as humanly possible. That is, right up to the moment they show up in school. Then their tune is changed—changed dramatically. School is boring; school is icky; school is work. Learning used to be play, it used to be about curiosity, and getting an answer to a question that I chose, and that helped me make sense of my world. But now it feels like you are trying to fill me up with useless scraps of information that I will never like and never use. And you punish me when I am not feeling well about myself or about school.

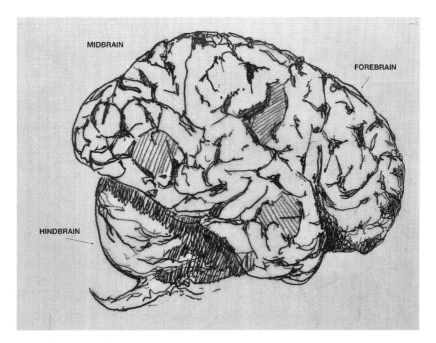

FIGURE 1.1 All Children Have Brains

Crisis in Academia

But it gets worse. In the US, a child drops out of high school every 26 seconds—that's more than a million children pushed out of school every year. That is costly, in more ways than might be apparent. It's more than a million children not contributing to society every year (2). Such dire dramas persist year in, year out . . . since we began collecting data in the middle of the last century. Research shows that the cost of dropouts is not only injurious to the students at the moment and for the rest of their lives, but that it has a very real collateral dollar impact on all taxpayers, and for the nation as a whole. For instance, the *Washington Alliance for Excellent Education* highlights the following impact of dropouts on society:

> If half the students who dropped out of the class of 2008 had graduated, they would have generated $4.8 million more in wages and $636 million in state and local taxes nationally in one average year of their working lives (adjusted to reflect today's costs).
>
> (3)

Expenses compound in a cycle of negative social and economic calamity. Impending expenses exacerbate individual and state "lost revenues," since the probability is also high that dropouts will end up incarcerated, use welfare, or live on food stamps (4). For instance, it costs significantly more to keep children in juvenile detention or in prison, than it does to educate them. A direct comparison in the state of Washington highlights that an incarcerated youth costs approximately $15,000 each year by comparison with $6,000 if attending public school (5).

And for a large population of children who manage to stay in school, the numbers with regard to their academic achievements are anything but spectacular. As shown in Figure 1.2 and Figure 1.3, scores indicating proficiency

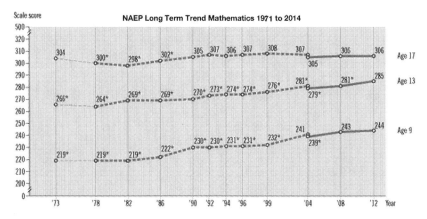

FIGURE 1.2 Nation's Report Card: 35-Year Trend in Mathematics

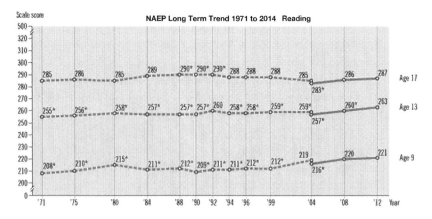

FIGURE 1.3 Nation's Report Card: 35-Year Trend in Reading

in math and reading have stagnated to 48% (give or take a few points) in 35 years. This is hard to credit in a country that has so much wealth, so much opportunity, spends so much per student, and has such aspirations for the individual within the free world. It makes no sense (6). Dissatisfaction at school adds up to squandered opportunities. The numbers are prohibitive; the cost astronomical. National Assessment of Educational Progress (NAEP) annual reports continue to churn out disappointing results and represent student lost potential (7).

A visceral background fear is an added crisis in today's learning environments. Students, guardians, and teachers are worried by school shootings and other violence that rob children of their potential in a system that is confused, broken, and seemingly stuck (8). Policy makers revert to two long-standing and popular solutions—more money and more technology (9), and have in recent years added a call for more mental health wellness and counseling (10). But the crisis persists. In addition, in most states youth suicide rates have been climbing (11). According to the American Academy of Pediatrics (AAP), youth suicide rates increased by 56% between the years 2000 and 2017 (12) a sad, grim fact that contributes to Americans' lower life expectancy.

Clear and tragic links have been drawn between dysfunctional classrooms and a robust school-to-prison pipeline (13), as well as to generational poverty and homelessness (10). Researchers who dig deep into questions of racial inequality between White and African American youth highlight findings that are staggering: severely high youth unemployment costs $10 billion in tax revenue each year at the federal and state level (14).

The sad reality is school sucks for at least 50% of kids! Ask them. School makes me . . . "Cry, sad, depressed, suicidal, anxious, feel like a failure, stupid." These are top results one gets when the question is aired on the web—regardless of search engine. At the same time, the other 50% either love or tolerate the exercise with equanimity. So what is going on? When we visit the same issues through a neural viewpoint, suddenly, it is less difficult to make sense of the apparent conundrums.

Intuition vs. Science

The neural outlook offered in this book "makes visible" the paradigm shift. Yet, this book is but a chapter. Most of what comes next will be created and co-created through practice by the very same teachers who were so reticent in the beginning. Paradigm shifts are hard. But wanting "more" involves undertaking a paradigm shift—actually several paradigm shifts at the same time. By adopting a neural vantage point in the classroom, teachers change along three axes. Intuition evolves into method when it is shown to have substantive scientific sustenance.

The three paradigms embrace three disciplines: Mindset, Expertise, and Motivation. Teachers already embrace many aspects of each paradigm. But intuition is not enough. In this book, we explore these three dimensions in greater detail, and from a neural perspective. A shift on three axes at the same time will deliver a completely different teacher, and a completely different learner.

So what do tennis balls have to do with any of this? It seems facetious and a little ridiculous to claim that two bouncing balls for every child solve American education. The short answer is that bouncing two balls alone is not sufficient intervention to solve American education. However, this simple exercise is ample evidence of a shifting paradigm that describes a route to solutions that are bringing meaningful change in classrooms every day. Teachers are reporting that their students are more engaged, more prepared for learning, and have found new joy in learning.

But, teachers have tried umpteen interventions sponsored by university education departments—prestigious, and intentioned, over the same 50 years that NAEP has been documenting stagnation and "flat lined" results. Why would this one be so different? Why would a paradigm shift of this simple nature have such different and palatable results?

Another no brainer! Only this time, it is the brain. A teacher who is prepared to introduce 50 lacrosse balls into her class first thing Monday morning is also the teacher who is thinking about "structure" before "function"; who is thinking about neurotransmitters instead of discipline; who is aware that there is no "good" behavior or "bad" behavior—it's just communication. And this teacher is aware that a trauma-centric, high ACEs child will have deficits in capacity for learning and concentration, for focus and attention—deficits that can easily be amended. She will also be mindful about which children are struggling, not because they are not good enough, but because they think they are not good enough. In other words, this teacher who begins her lesson with deliberate attention to physical activity has shifted along three paradigm continuums at the same time. This teacher has proved the paradigm shift in his own life (and for his own children) first, and is then ready and capable of delivering it to students.

This teacher knows the import of myelination, cognitive rehearsal, and long-term potentiation. What teacher gets up each day and thinks to herself, "I am going to grow my student's SLF today. The new connections will help them thrive." Back to front, and left to right; this teacher is cognizant of super "highways" of connectivity that are part of the SLF (Superior Longitudinal Fasciculus) and corpus callosum. These myelinated white-matter tracts connect the cerebellum at the back of the brain with the child's executive function at the front of the brain. She is also particularly intentional about giving the children opportunities to cross the midline and strengthen white-matter connections in the corpus callosum. This strengthening of the left and right hemispheric connector circuits increases the child's capacity for processing information and problem solving.

The critical difference is "knowing" about the learning brain versus knowing about good and bad behaviors. Intuitively, many teachers have, over the years, accomplished amazing feats of mental dexterity for their students using only extrinsic rewards and punishment methods. But when a teacher discovers the science behind why a particular procedure will always work better this way . . . and a particular practice can never work with these students . . . then they experience a paradigm shift to a cognitive world that makes sense. All three axes of the paradigm shift are reciprocal and mutually synergistic. "Mindset" enhances and elaborates "Expertise" and "Motivation," in the same way that "Expertise" enhances and elaborates "Mindset" and "Motivation."

Mindset, Expertise, and Motivation become implicit elements of a cognitive way of teaching that we describe in this book. Mindset is not new to classrooms, but a "neural" application offers a refreshing perspective. Expertise rarely shows up on the teacher's radar, but a neural assessment on routine vs. adaptive allows the student to thrive on 21st century skills. Shifting from extrinsic to intrinsic has always been an aspiration, difficult to accomplish in an extrinsic model. The view through a neural pane makes this shift not only attainable but, also, imminently desirable.

Figures 1.4 through 1.7 describe an iterative progression of the three-axes paradigm shift and what it accomplishes when it is perfected simultaneously. Dweck's work (15) shown in Figure 1.4 highlights a continuum from Fixed to Growth. Naturally, everyone claims a growth mindset, but, in fact, saying it and knowing how to achieve a growth mindset without a neural advantage is quite challenging.

The second construct focuses on Expertise, Y-axis in Figure 1.5. It, too, is depicted as a continuum from Routine to Adaptive. Hatano and Inagaki's (16) work in this field highlights the difference between people who simply swell the ranks of incompetent or mediocre functionaries, and people who exceed the envelope of creativity and potential.

The third dimension centers on a critical aspect of adolescent learning and, subsequently, success in life—Motivation. Most people can recite

FIGURE 1.4 Paradigm Shift in One Dimension

FIGURE 1.5 Paradigm Shift in Two Dimensions

positive attributes about the value of "intrinsic" motivation, and insist that such a fundamental impetus is vital for learning. However, paying lip service to the ideal, and achieving it, are worlds apart. More critical is the realization that attempting to be intrinsic in an extrinsic school environment is almost impossible. Many teachers have foundered on this craggy outcrop, trying to illuminate a personal love of learning at the same time as disciplining the child for a bad attitude towards learning. It doesn't compute.

This shift is shown in Figure 1.6, the Z-axis emphasizes a continuum from Extrinsic to Intrinsic. A rich motivation literature highlights the difference

X axis = Mindset [Fixed → Growth]
Y axis = Expertise [Routine → Adaptive]
Z axis = Motivation [Extrinsic → Intrinsic]

FIGURE 1.6 Paradigm Shift in Three Dimensions

between intrinsic and extrinsic (*17*). We focus on teachers acquiring the knowledge to implement it in schools.

Finally, in Figure 1.7, teachers demonstrate what happens when they integrate the implied cognitive move. It's a three-dimensional cube-like model in which individuals can place themselves visually in relation to any construct in any time. For instance, I can be fixed in relation to how I like my coffee, but willing to accept your desire to brew it in a different way. This tolerance for ambiguity is central to being adaptive in a fast-paced, competitive world.

Individuals who start out Fixed, Routine, and Extrinsic begin a journey, which has the capability to deliver them as thinkers of a different hue— Growth, Adaptive, and Intrinsic. It sounds weird, but teachers get it immediately. Growth Mindset means I understand plasticity and my brain has incredible potential. Adaptive expertise means I embrace 21st century skills by stepping outside my comfort zone. I am capable of taking risks with new information and ready to learn from my peers. Intrinsic motivation means that I understand and ensure that students experience autonomy; I facilitate opportunities for mastery, and am deliberate about fostering a sense of purpose. The constructs Mindset, Expertise, and Motivation are everyday constituents of education and learning, but when attention is directed to their particular attributes and competencies, new effective and affective outcomes are realized (*18*).

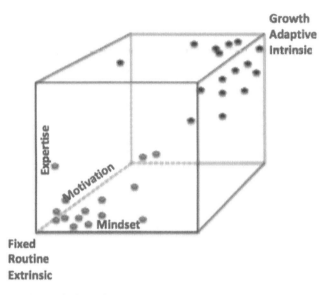

FIGURE 1.7 Paradigm Shift in Three Dimensions at the Same Time

All three constructs, though independent, connect synergistically in a way that enhances each other singly and in tandem. For instance, a growth mindset feeds the idea of autonomy and mastery for intrinsic motivation, and a sense of purpose supports a growth mindset given that malleability of structure underpins development and function. Together, Growth, Adaptive, and Intrinsic facilitate conceptual collisions, and foster a convergence of energy, skill, and drive.

2

Rewards Work . . . Sometimes

I was surprised to learn that rewarding some kids means punishing other kids.
—*Middle School Teacher*

For many children, the learning years are not working out so successfully. Hating everything about school is not the ideal setting for reaching one's potential. Data confirm this observation. It's no secret that academic performance has stagnated for a long time. Every October, the *Nation's Report Card* delivers a long list of disappointing numbers representing student academic achievement. A review going back to when data was first collected by NAEP verifies a flat-lined graph year after year since 1969 (7). Scientists from many fields suggest far-flung reasons for such a dire state of affairs; reasons that range from high-stakes tests, to class size, and lack of money (19). The crisis persists, as the US (20) and other countries (10) sink deeper into a despairing morass (21). Compounding these issues is the sad fact that youth suicide rates climb higher year over year (11).

Children are labeled and stratified in school. In any classroom, children know who is the A student and who struggles, who is "best" learner and who is "troublemaker." They know who is "Free and Reduced," who is "Gifted," and who is 'Title One.' In addition, because of prescribed methods and frameworks, learners are categorized into three groups based on behavior: (i) Compliant, (ii) At Risk, and (iii) High Risk, or simply Tier One, Tier Two, and Tier Three. Stratification highlights achievement gaps, gender inequities, and rising inequalities in day-to-day classroom occurrences that are very troubling for every generation of school goers (*22, 23*).

A New Learning World

Behavior is the root of stratification. And behavior is Skinner territory. For him, the brain was a "black box." In order to do rigorous experimentation with regard to learning, it was only possible to measure what was going in (stimulus), and what was coming out (response). A burgeoning science of experimental psychology gave him the opportunity to discover "laws" and "rules" that seemed to describe learning. Behaviorism was an obvious shoe-in that tried to answer some big educational questions—questions, which had challenged thinkers for centuries (*24*). What governed language acquisition? Could we explain human behavior? How best to set up public education for the masses? Could these be bundled into a tidy nuclear packet—an elegant unified theory—that somehow underpinned pedagogy?

Yet, during the heyday of Skinnerian behaviorism, many experts questioned his stimulus-response ideologies, which did not fully answer niggling questions relating to language acquisition, nor indeed schooling. Critics were quick to point out that he studied arbitrary animal behavior in laboratory settings, rather than specific behaviors typical of children in natural environments (*25*). In addition, the linguist Noam Chomsky surfaced a "paucity of stimulus" argument that challenged Skinner's dictum that all language was derived externally from environmental factors (*26*). Chomsky, in the Cartesian tradition, argued that learning was (i) innate, (ii) internal, and (iii) universal. In spite of its widespread implementation, it turns out that most teachers are rather "fuzzy" in their thinking about what the difference between classical conditioning, operant conditioning, and stimulus response conditions that claim to define causal links with behavior and learning.

Stimulus Response Conditioning in the Classroom

When there is only one model—we are compelled to construct systems that fit that model, where the "law of the instrument" contributes to a contrived moment that fosters cognitive bias and pressure to deliver (*27*). In other words, in a one-model world, the man with the "hammer" sees only "nails" (*28*) and, in a stimulus-response classroom, outcomes must look a lot like scripted behaviorist schemas. What is it like to get under the hood to view the structures that define operant conditioning? How did a science of learning evolve from a schema that offers little consideration for mentalistic models, introspection, or innate capacity (29)?

Skinner's research described a fundamental scientific principle, which has dominated educational practice, since the middle of the last century. According to his findings, higher response rates followed rewards, and lower response rates followed punishments. He was able to define a schedule of "reinforcements" to influence the rate of response. From this, stimulus-response reinforcement schedules were intentionally introduced into teacher preparation courses and came to widely influence how children were taught. Skinner differed from Pavlov and Thorndike by stating that an animal's response rates were dependent upon what happened "after," rather than "before" the stimulus.

Skinner did not consider "punishment" an effective methodology for training animals, teaching children, or managing public offenders (30), yet punishment has become the primary method used in schools and in places of incarceration. How, then, did teaching and learning get so enamored with rewards and punishments? Reinforcement (Skinner preferred "reinforcement" over "reward") and punishment, the core tools of operant conditioning, are either positive (delivered following a response), or negative (withdrawn following a response). Figure 2.1 describes the method that is so ingrained in our schools.

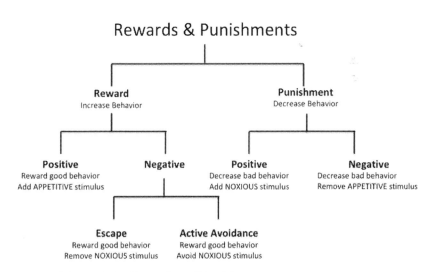

FIGURE 2.1 Schematic for Rewards and Punishments

Most teacher training programs define techniques, strategies, and methods that are adopted piecemeal or in whole for managing classrooms; getting children to behave in a way that is socially acceptable. And in addition, most guardians expect schools to reinforce good behavior and to punish bad behavior. This common criterion for classroom management is provisioned in order to (i) eliminate disruptive behavior, and (ii) limit dysfunction. Teachers are trained to prevent individual "trouble makers" from disrupting the flow of lesson plans, and from distracting other children's attention and focus—essentially, to allow all children to access the system and make progress unimpeded.

The big idea is straightforward—strength of any behavior is modified by reinforcement—positive reinforcement or negative reinforcement. "Good" behavior is desirable; "bad" behavior is undesirable. The rule is simple. Reinforcement for a desired behavior is intended to increase that behavior. Negative reinforcement for an undesirable behavior is intended to decrease that behavior. On the surface, such a schema looks doable and actionable. Most people can relate to rewards for behaviors that they might repeat. Conversely, they can relate to being punished for bad behaviors with a view to eliminate them. It seems to make sense.

Based on teacher and learner experience with the rewards and punishments model, it quickly becomes clear that there is a lot more to the concept of "rewards and punishment" than meets the eye. By drilling down into its constituent parts, we uncover a hidden nature of processes involved. We examine mental gyrations that result by unpacking neural substrates that foster social and emotional outcomes.

Though it might seem implicit, it comes as a surprise for many teachers to realize that there is a positive and a negative aspect to each side of a Skinner equation:

- *Positive reinforcement/Negative reinforcement* (Add a stimulus/Remove a stimulus)
- *Positive punishment/Negative punishment* (Add a stimulus/Remove a stimulus)

It might even seem paradoxical—the notion that one has to add a stimulus for positive reinforcement, and to remove a stimulus for negative reinforcement. In Skinner's laboratory, a stimulus is described as appetitive (tasty, desirable), or aversive (noxious, undesirable).

One must add an appetitive stimulus, or remove (or avoid) a noxious stimulus, for positive reinforcement. One must add a noxious stimulus for positive punishment and remove an appetitive stimulus for negative punishment. Food is synonymous with the concept of appetitive. Hunger can increase the effectiveness of food as an appetitive stimulus. A noxious stimulus speaks to an aversive moment. It's about stimulus: appetitive or aversive. Everything is binary: add/remove; good/bad.

A positive reward is the most obvious and most desirable for reinforcing good behavior. The schema for Rewards is shown in Figure 2.2. Adding or removing stimuli accounts for positive and negative aspects of a "reinforcer." Ask any pet owner who has trained a puppy to lie down and roll over in exchange for a treat. With consistent reinforcement, the puppy will soon get the message that the work has to come before the treat.

This idea of increasing good behavior with rewards is pervasive in schools, where a child might be rewarded with a "star" or a good grade when an assignment is turned in. At home, the child might be rewarded with a cookie for tidying her room.

Removing or avoiding a noxious stimulus is also seen as a way to increase good behavior. Escape unwelcome interruption of an alarm clock by pressing the snooze button, thus **removing** the stimulus. Similarly, every child recognizes Active Avoidance when they work hard, in order to avoid a bad grade.

While both these responses to everyday stimuli are clearly prominent in our lives and often bring about specified desired behavior, we must admit

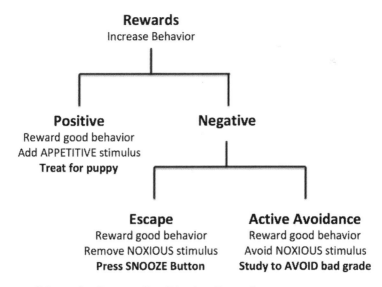

FIGURE 2.2 Schema for Operant Conditioning: Rewards

that both these events cast motivation into a reactive state. Studying in order to avoid a bad grade is not the reason children attend school. The notion of reinforcement is not only injurious to sensitive learners; it is a constant contributor to children's "boredom" and cognitive fatigue (31). Modern learning sciences distinguish repetition (behaviorist) from cognitive rehearsal (cognitivist). Academic journals highlight how learning happens and how best to take advantages of powerful pre- and post-synaptic plasticity enhancers that regulate long-term potentiation (32). Thus, from a neural stance, repetition is to reinforcement as cognitive rehearsal is to long-term potentiation.

Neuroscience is clear. While the behaviorist setting is all about "reinforcers," it turns out that reinforce is a construct that is meaningless in the world of neuroscience. There is no "reinforcer" gene. There is no "reinforcer" neuron. Learning scientists are only now beginning to adopt new models in order to get past the mechanistic science and ruthless reduction (33) associated with behaviorism. New models are needed if we are to engage the limitless complexity of a child's learning mind.

Teacher Talk

Incremental nuance and iterative cycles of practice deliver change just as easily as a cataclysmic event. For change to occur, there needs to be fundamental shifts at a molecular state. Here, we listen to teachers who have experienced change because they made the fundamental shift from a rewards/punishment mindset to a cognitivist approach. This is not as easy as simply saying "I want to be a cognitivist." It requires very real, if subtle, shifts in thinking, vocabulary, and action.

We are confident that teachers, who make small changes, will see immediate positive impact. Experience has shown that tiny shifts in internal mental models ultimately deliver large changes in how we approach teaching. Mental models suffice to get started. Evidence points to the importance of teacher mindset as they approach classroom instruction (34). We have witnessed successful teachers persist and demand more. Cognitive surpasses rewards/punishment; intrinsic surpasses extrinsic. When lesson plans work and discipline referrals drop off, a teacher's life gets easier. Students are pleased with successful outcomes, and guardians are happy to support the improved effort. It sets in motion a positive spiral of events.

Teachers answer three scaffolding questions that "make visible" their thinking in a co-creative space with regard to a neural engagement. As we begin to make sense of this lens against our knowledge and experience, we acknowledge just one thing. If this method and model didn't work, teachers wouldn't be insisting on the new catchword for their colleagues. **NEURAL UP!!**

What was Surprising?
Teacher #1

Many things in this chapter surprised me. The idea that we have been stuck in a teaching and learning model that is basically flawed is not only surprising, it makes me angry.

Teacher #2

I was surprised to learn that teachers who adopt the cognitive model spend less time in lesson planning, less time in managing the classroom, and more time doing things that are way more meaningful for their work and personal lives. I wish we had known this sooner. I feel I have lost years of my life doing a job that was essentially half-baked.

What we already knew but now see in a new way?
Teacher #1

I already knew that rewards were not working, but now I can see why. It seems totally weird that we were so easily lead to focus on rewards, like stars, and stickers, and grades, when we knew deep down that these were extrinsic motivators. Yet, ask any teacher— intrinsic motivation is key to meaningful learning. How could I have managed to equate a gold star with intrinsic motivation? I think it was just wishful thinking.

Teacher #2

I already knew that results were inching down year over year for a long time, but I had not made the connection to methods. In retrospect, it is clearly the case. It saddens me to think that my efforts were ineffective in spite of my best diligence and countless hours.

What we need help with?

Teacher #1

We desperately need to know how to transition from a behaviorist model to a neuro cognitive model. What does that look like? Where do we start?

Teacher #2

We would like more evidence and papers to read about the shift from extrinsic to intrinsic motivation.

Big question for me is, "How do I teach without rewards?" I thought kids love rewards.

Strategies for Change

Teachers are universally pleased beyond measure when the light bulb lights up for children. Intuitively, teachers have known for a long time that stickers, stars, incessant "atta-boy" praise and the ever present A or A+ grade is not necessarily the best way to teach children. In future chapters, we will explain why it is important to praise the effort not the child, why rewards never work for some children, and, why it doesn't matter whether we reward or punish other children.

Simple Strategies

1. **What Part of Brain?** When washing your teeth each morning, try standing on one foot for up to 30 seconds. What part(s) of your brain are you using?
2. **How does my Brain?** When flossing your teeth each morning, notice how you can turn your attention to the left side of any molar and then recognize the opposite right side. How can your brain distinguish the edge of one tooth from the next?

Radical Strategies

1. **Celebrate Successes!** Instead of using IEPs try using PIEs. In a later strategy, session we will explain what we mean by that idea.

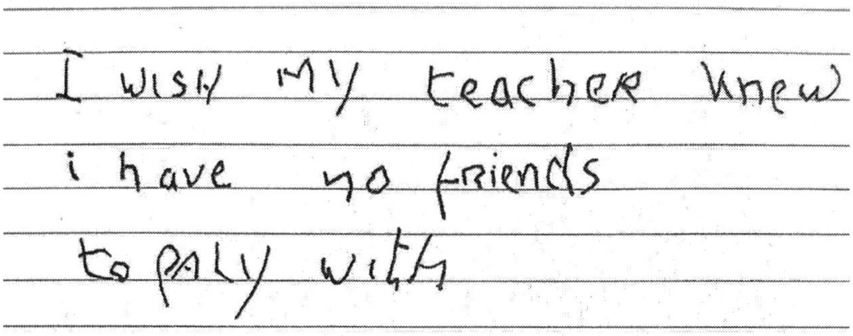
I wish my teacher knew
i have no friends
to paly with

FIGURE 2.3 I Wish My Teacher Knew . . .

Meanwhile, play with the concept and see why IEPs do not work. It's a matter of focusing on what the child CAN do instead of what the child CAN'T do . . . yet.

2. **I Wish My Teacher Knew . . .** As seen in Figure 2.3, give children time to write (or draw pictures) that allow them to make visible what they want their teacher to know about them. Be prepared for amazing results.

Summary

In this chapter, we reviewed the science behind why the construct of "reward" is nebulous at best, and, for most kids, scary, and oppressive. In a later chapter, we learn that for at least 50% of our students, neither rewards nor punishments work. And for the remaining 50% (who are highly resilient), it doesn't matter whether we reward or punish them.

Vocabulary

Cognitivist, Behaviorist, Intrinsic Motivation

3

Teach With A Instead of E

If I do something and I feel good, I do more of it . . . Law of Affect

—Thorndike, 1903

When Edward Lee Thorndike stumbled upon the first law of learning in 1903—the **Law of Affect**—the world of schools and teaching was changed forever. This Law of Affect, simply stated, looked like this: "If I do something and it feels good, I'll do more of it; if I do something, and it feels bad, I'll do less of it." It described a bond between actions and feelings. The greater the "satisfaction" or "discomfort," the greater the strengthening or weakening of the bond. The focus for this first law was on the word **Affect**, deliberately spelled with A. The actions described produced feelings—satisfactory feelings or discomforting feelings—which resulted from affective change in the nervous system. The problem was the cat! In 1898, cats weren't supposed to have feelings.

Although Thorndike, in his 1898 monograph, *Animal Intelligence: An Experimental Study of the Associate Processes in Animals*, was willing to explore the question of kitten feelings, he was not willing to go public with it. His question was, however, indicative of his thinking process: "Does the kitten feel the 'sound of call, memory-image of milk in a saucer in the kitchen (35)?'" At that time, psychologists were not prepared to admit that animals had feelings.

Thorndike replaced A with E—Affect became Effect. Today, teachers in preparatory courses learn about Thorndike's Law of Effect. In other words, Affect (emotions and feelings) is not the center of teacher preparation, but Effect (causal result) is. Thorndike's revision introduced deep and lasting consequences for education that persist to this day. As shown in Figure 3.1, Thorndike's contribution to education is recognized to this day.

Semantically, Affect is very different from Effect. The meaning is further complicated because Affect and Effect are used interchangeably to denote outcomes. As verb (Affect), and noun (Effect), both words describe results. In psychology, however, especially educational and cognitive psychology, affect refers to emotions, moods, and feelings. And, therein, lay Thorndike's dilemma. In 1903, it wasn't proper to admit that a hungry Cheshire cat could express emotions or feelings. His moody cat, infamous in learning lore, was the intrepid feline who figured out how to escape a carefully contrived puzzle box (36).

FIGURE 3.1 Author at Thorndike Hall Teachers College, NY

The Behaviorist Classroom

In the burgeoning psychology of learning, John Watson, godfather of behaviorism, and B. F. Skinner, who ratcheted it up to a radical behaviorism, designed rigorous methods for studying inputs and outputs associated with learning. Since they had no access to the human brain, their solution was to focus effort on inputs—observable stimuli from the environment and link them to outputs—observable behaviors of animals. Words were chosen to describe the experiments. "Satisfaction" was arbitrarily changed to "Reinforcement;" "Discomfort" was arbitrarily changed to "Punishment."

That was then. Today, with advanced imagining techniques, previously unobservable neural structures that underlie mental processes are no longer invisible. Thanks to 3D modeling like Diffusion Tensor Imaging and Tractography, neuroscientists know quite a bit more than Watson, Skinner, or Thorndike about how the brain works (33). It is indeed time to revisit Thorndike's Law of Effect, to restore the original A that aligns with children's autonomic nervous system emotions and feelings. What can neuroscience tell us today about feelings and learning?

Today, scientists can examine central nervous system gustatory sensory organs to learn about for example, the tongue's receptors for taste—umami, sweetness, saltiness, bitterness, and sourness. So too can we look at receptors, synapses, and structures that govern feelings in learning. As imaging technologies improve, mysteries surrounding learning recede. A critical canonical principal states that what came first forms a foundation for what comes after. Brain builds from bottom to top, from back to front.

At "primordial" lower-level processing (brain stem), the child will experience evolutionary memories—involuntary actions that we cannot choose to avoid. A typical response to a threat, fear, or imminent danger (real or imagined) results in amygdala hijack. Teachers will testify that these reactive responses are daily occurrences. Primal, involuntary behaviors are at the same level as homeostatic affects that activate with hunger, thirst, and regulation of the body. Sensory affects are very common in classrooms. Children love sweet things, shiny things, and colorful mobiles from the external world that deliver "nice" feelings. Most classrooms are filled with sensory activators.

Above primary lower-level processes, secondary affect processes are located in the midbrain. Pavlov's classical conditioning, a deeply unconscious affective process, occurs in this region. For instance, the child who, upon hearing the front door slam, immediately experiences physiological changes in his nervous system through Amygdala activation, because he associates the sound of the door slamming with dad showing up in a violent, drunken state. It's a deeply unconscious state that the child cannot avoid.

In this midbrain space also we locate Skinner's operant conditioning. Here, stimuli connect with the reward system in the Nucleus Accumbens. The child will respond to a reward in a reflective way by association with past memories. Here, too, are habituation processes (Dorsal Striatum), which involve emotions that parse "affect" into space and time. This is how the brain manages stress, so it is not so overwhelming. Stressors become moments in time based on danger "signals" and safety "signals." Such memories tied to emotions are essential for building a system of affective regulation— establishes an affective connection with teachers who can scaffold co- and self- regulatory processes.

Above secondary "affect" processes we enter the "awareness" world in the prefrontal cortex. Most children spend a large part of their mental world in awareness—they know that they are experiencing things. Here, in the neocortex, they are able to think, plan, and predict. This, too, is where they experience emotional ruminations and inhibitions. Together with emotional supports, this higher-order processing capability is key to regulation. With guidance, children are able to reflect on alternatives for the future, based on memories of the recent past (self-regulation).

Thorndike's dichotomous dilemma (Effect trumps Affect) exists in class- rooms everywhere. If teachers approach their tasks with results (Effect) as the measure of success, it is easy to set up a system of assessment that looks like high-stakes tests. If, on the other hand, they approach their tasks with emo- tional maturity (Affect) as the measure of success, school looks entirely dif- ferent. Sense of belonging, safety, and social-emotional frameworks assume an uppermost status in teachers' mindsets and method. When educators try to do both in a fragmented system, neither works satisfactorily. This, unfor- tunately, is how we experience the incoherent legacy of Thorndike.

Today, neural educators interpret Thorndike from a cognitive perspective. A nuanced understanding of Affect vs. Effect makes all the difference. Since Thorndike's fateful adjustment in spelling, student academic outcomes have been saddled with "impassive" results, as opposed to "ardent" emotions; with products instead of processes; and, with functions instead of structures. No wonder we find dismal results October after October in the Nation's Report Card (7). It's not the children; it's not teachers; it's Effect over Affect.

Yes, of course there are enlightened exceptions where play, fun, and emo- tional support are dominant themes in classrooms—intuitive processes from amazing teachers—not from fundamental principles of learning science. But, occasional "intuitive" respite from drudgery is not enough. Schools can be experienced as negative, punitive, and exclusionary "push-out" spaces, where many children fail to achieve their potential.

The Cognitive Classroom

A neuroscience lens applied to Thorndike's legacy is consummately revealing. The 30,000-foot view describes an evolutionary structure of the brain in three functional regions. The oldest part is often referred to as "reptilian" hindbrain situated at the base of the head. Above that, a newer region (midbrain) is the seat of emotions and feelings. The most recent (neocortex) is located in the forehead where higher-order thinking and conscious "awareness" resides.

In the classroom, each child has a well-developed reptilian brain, a less well-developed emotional brain, and an even less well-developed neocortex. That, of course, is the reason for school. Connecting and growing these three brain regions is also the reason that it takes roughly 25 years to raise a child to maturity. It takes time and effort to connect the three brain regions into a cohesive functioning unit. Teachers and guardians facilitate this growth—reactive reptilian, to ardent emotional, to executive thinking brain—by building circuits, providing cognitive rehearsal for myelination, and strengthening structures for identity and potential. Each child communicates via the neocortex, but lives in the ancient recesses of the survival mind when alone or in social contexts (33). And social context is all about school—it is all about emotions. "Am I good enough?" "Can I survive this new thing?" "What will happen next?"

We revisit and explore further into the three evolutionary regions of the brain in Chapter 6. But for now, it's sufficient to recognize that each child experiences these three regions to varying degrees.

The child's passions, intense feelings, and emotions arise from the primitive brain. Primary processes come first because they are rooted in survival. It follows that what comes first guides what comes second. Each child lives in a primitive mind in the primary processing hind region. All newer processes are dependent on these primary processes. Thus, stemming from each child's evolutionary adaptations, behaviors are reflected in primary affective systems. Feelings matter! The child will experience play impulses, survival impulses, fear activations, and safety impulses. Children are easy prey to deep-seated reactions like fear, anger, and frustration from the ancient recesses of that reptilian, survival brain. All children first seek a sense of belonging to allay the survival urge.

Next, the child will experience secondary processing in the emotional midbrain. Careful guidance and co-regulation in this region will help the child begin a process of self-awareness and self-regulation. Sense of belonging is vital here, also. Every child needs, at least, four consistently caring adults to shepherd them though this emotional morass (37).

Finally, access to the child's executive functioning area delivers awareness in the tertiary processing neocortex. As humans, we seek connection and emotional interaction in structures of the midbrain. And up front, the neocortex allows us to articulate thoughts and desires, predictions, and plans that are deeply rooted in emotional and survival instincts.

Competing Models

Thus, we identify two competing learning models. The first and oldest is a behaviorist "rewards and punishments" framework that has long established, and deeply entrenched, itself in the culture of schools, home, and workplaces. We also highlight an intellectual and emotional approach that springs from cognitive psychology and neuroscience. Some teachers have shifted to the new paradigm. They reject the older entrenched model by abandoning methods that use rewards and punishments and by embracing a neural perspective that focuses on (i) intrinsic motivation, (ii) adaptive expertise, and (iii) growth mindset. In this section, we explore implications for a preference for one model over the other. Unfortunately, when teachers try to be in both camps, the implications are profound and dramatic.

Skinner replaced Pavlov and Thorndike as the pre-eminent authority on learning for most of the last century. And, like educational psychologists who were beginning to grasp the elements of learning sciences, he was interested in questions relating to knowledge acquisition, knowledge retention, and forgetting. According to Skinner's doctrine, education is what survives when what has been learned has been forgotten (25).

Skinner was following in the footsteps of the prominent 19th century experimental psychologist Herman Ebbinghaus, who investigated questions surrounding memory and the "forgetting" phenomenon (38). His work showed that up to 90% of what people learn is forgotten within a few days. In fact, the majority of this forgetting occurs in the first few hours.

Ebbinghaus' findings have been robustly confirmed in modern times. Skinner was able to demonstrate with reinforcement and extinction techniques that learning did indeed accede to routines of Ebbibnghaus' infamous Forgetting Curve (see Figure 3.2). Sadly, Ebinghaus' Forgetting Curve is alive and well in classrooms everywhere. Most of what children learn in school appears to be forgotten before they get home. We know better today. A neural perception together with methods, which are informed by how the brain works, will quickly reverse Ebbinghaus' Forgetting Curve by fostering practices that are metacognitive, collaborative, and generative (39).

Every child interacts with, and makes sense of, incoming sensory data. Sensory data might be visual, auditory, tactile, taste, smell, or some combination. By changing incoming focus, the information will be received in

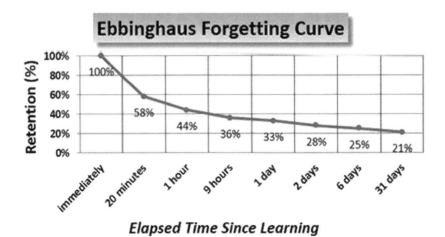

FIGURE 3.2 Ebbinghaus Describes a Forgetting Curve

a different way. If the focus is on "content," we can anticipate the "Effect" outcome; if the focus is on learner, together with their emotional and survival baggage, there can be a different "Affect" outcome. Teachers are often intuitive about how to balance content with context, learner with learning, so that the best outcomes can occur. Unfortunately, in spite of what the intuitive teacher can accomplish, sometimes "less than desired" outcomes result; the learner can become obstreperous, distracted, disruptive, and even aggressive. From a neural standpoint, said "unexpected" behaviors are actually "expected" behaviors.

These latter outcomes being less desirable, children are labeled and stratified into one of the three categories described earlier: (i) compliant, (ii) at risk, or (iii) high risk. Teachers lament children's "readiness" for learning. Many solutions have become normalized in school settings over the years. These include IEPs, low grade scores (C-minus, D, or NG) detentions, punishments, as well as tutoring, extra-curricular classes, test-prep classes, and a host of study aids that are expensive and time consuming.

Teacher Talk

A Generation-Z (iGeneration) child is tech enabled, digital, and anything but binary. Fast processors, they tend to be equally comfortable in multi-level gaming and blended-learning environments. In fact, today's classrooms are mostly in the cloud. Fast-processing children can think easily in three- and four-dimensional space (40). These learners find it difficult to trim their wings—zone down to a two-dimensional educational system that is expressly binary—right/wrong, sit here/not there, shut up/listen, don't interrupt/follow instructions, get a good grade, zero tolerance/suspension. School is boring for fast processors. And boring is the same as high stress. Children experience amygdala hijack with boredom.

Successes with cognitive models provide solid evidence that this new practice shifts learning environments dramatically. Next, are first-hand accounts from teachers who successfully applied a neural lens to their classroom learning spaces. Miss W is a health and fitness teacher who didn't discover "neuroscience of learning" until she had struggled more than a decade managing, against all odds, to bring order to a world of learners that was dominated by stress, trauma, and failure. Today, she works in an alternative high school with children who have been "pushed out" of the traditional system. This is their last refuge; a final hope to reach for their potential.

> I'm finishing up the most amazing quarter of my teaching career. These kids are desperate for success. They have been the underdogs for so long; they don't see how they will ever experience success. My expectations became much higher with the neural lens, and the kids left ignited after their final exam!!! It was beautiful . . . I've changed everything that I have ever done. Threw out the old model. My kids left my class this week feeling successful . . . real hard work success. It's not about STEM; it's about working memory and executive function. Yes, this has been life changing. Seriously.
>
> (Middle School Teacher, 2017)

So why do rewards work only sometimes? Rewards should work every time. . . . Right? But they do not. In fact, most children didn't trust rewards. They associated them with punishments. Here is a first-hand account from Miss W.

> At first, rewards had great promise. I gave them stars and stickers at every opportunity. I was careful to say good things to the children at least six times every class. But not long into the school year, I realized that the rewards were being met with emptiness and anger. I doubled down in my resolve. It got worse. Soon the children weren't engaging at all—even the ones that were doing ok a few weeks earlier. What was I doing wrong?

A few weeks later, she had an opportunity for a one-on-one conversation with Bree, one of the children who wasn't shunning her . . . yet. She decided to ask the 50-million-dollar-question.

> Bree, why are your classmates ignoring the rewards and the good things I say about them every day?
>
> You broke their trust.
>
> What? What do you mean? I never broke their trust; I say very positive things about their work every hour. I am careful to not break their trust.
>
> At the start of the year, we all liked you. You were fun and we trusted you . . . You were different. We looked forward to your class . . . we even liked the rewards that you handed out. I still have that sticker that you gave me "**BEST DAY EVER**" I like it still. But very soon, you began sending Marie into Timeout, Susan to the principal's office, Joe was kicked into the corridor, and Rachel was expelled for three days . . . and Michael was kicked out of school all together."
>
> Yes. But they broke all the class rules. We have to have rules. There are consequences for bad behavior. I didn't want to kick Michael out. But there is a no tolerance . . .
>
> Yes. We know that. But when you began punishing us, we didn't trust your rewards either. It looked a lot like home. We knew that one day soon, you would do to any of us what you did to Michael, and Marie, and Rachel, and Susan, and . . . and . . .
>
> But you are not Michael; you are not Susan. How can you think that I would treat you the same way?

There was no answer for this question . . . at least not until she discovered the neuroscience of teaching. Then she began to equate rewards and punishments as one and the same thing.

She began to change her classroom management vocabulary from words like bad behavior, consequences, and zero tolerance. She replaced them with words like amygdala hijack, reactive, involuntary, a brain where freeze, fight and flight resides, intrinsic motivation and myelination for new structures. Very soon she was devouring every paper she could lay her hands on that discussed issues about structure before function, long-term potentiation, and reticular activating system. The result was immediate and dramatic. It changed her teaching career and enhanced her students' life trajectories.

4

Punishments Work . . . Sometimes

I don't like it when a teacher punishes my friend

—*High School Student*

Punishment in school is synonymous with discipline. It shouldn't be, but unfortunately it is. The etymology of discipline clearly connects it with disciple, an ardent follower, a learner, a pupil, or a student. Would that our student learners were ardent followers of the learning process. Instead, discipline is equated with the practice of training children to obey rules and a prescribed code of behavior. Teachers are taught to use punishment to enforce accepted patterns of behavior and to correct disobedience and unruly behavior—thus perfecting moral character. Since they are responsible for the welfare of all children in their care, that responsibility has an eminently practical function—that of deterring harmful behavior (41).

Corporal punishment is prohibited in Head Start programs and in most juvenile detention facilities (42), yet, it is still legal to physically punish children in at least 19 states. Many guardians and teachers recognize the following intention of punishment. It is defined by educational practice as: deliberate infliction of physical pain by hitting, paddling, spanking, slapping, or any other physical force used "as a means of discipline (43)."

The object is usually to reduce aggressive and/or disruptive behavior in the classroom, and to improve learning outcomes for all students by controlling children who are "misbehaving." Most forms of punishment are acceptable as long as "discipline" is the outcome—many programs include the word discipline in their title. In theory, this is a legitimate and well-meaning goal. But as most teachers will confirm, it rarely works (44).

Teachers are skilled in managing unruly children—children who typically have difficulty focusing, staying on task, and who inadvertently disrupt other learners. They use a generous selection of behavior modification tools to bring these children into line, including reminders, praise, gentle nudges, body language, and unspoken "eye-catching" stares that indicate boundaries, and so on. In so doing, many teachers gain a reputation as "strict," "severe," "stern," or "austere." At the same time, other teachers gain reputations as 'lenient,' 'soft,' 'kind,' 'forgiving,' or 'tolerant.' From the standpoint of the student, school can become a constant "cat and mouse" game that is going to end badly for the mouse at some point.

Expected Behavior

Schools are amazingly successful at "pushing out" disruptive children, forcing them to miss out on educational opportunities (45). Once the cycle is initiated, children tend to fall farther and farther behind—thus, defeating the purpose of the intervention in the first place. It is a lose-lose situation that has been documented in many countries where ugly outcomes persist once the cycle of neglect is set in motion (10).

A neural lens sees children as developing brains; errant "outbursts" is expected behavior! That same neural lens interprets all behavior as simply communication. If the child is acting out, acting up, is aggressive, and so on, then the neural lens will immediately recognize the reactive output of an amygdala hijack and will choose immediate remedies that work. When students are driven by "Trauma" and "ACEs," readiness for learning is seriously impeded. If children were more compliant, less obnoxious, pay better attention, and, in short, "apply" themselves, then they would be welcome in classrooms.

Forms of punishment exist that do not involve physical pain. They reside in a psychosocial, mentalistic mode that prove to be as (or even more) damaging for developing brains (46). In this respect, punishment is the quintessential "personalized" learning program, and is sadly delinquent in terms of academic outcomes and better student engagement (47).

In a previous chapter, we uncovered the precariousness of "rewards" associated with a persistent reinforcement aspect of Skinner's operant conditioning model. In attempts to understand the "inputs and outputs" of the human brain, he settled on a theory that didn't involve seeing inside the brain. In so doing, Skinner worked from the assumption that unobservable events obey the same laws as observable events. Skinner's position was simply that the ultimate causes of behavior are located in an organism's individual history, and in the species evolutionary history, not in the brain (48). Skinner was recognized by many prestigious bodies for his contribution to mankind (48). He would probably be immensely disappointed today to observe how classrooms conflate stimulus response, operant conditioning, and rewards and punishments with little regard to the science behind how or why they work or not.

Punishment Model

Following Skinner's model, punishments are rendered positive or negative by giving or taking away a stimulus. To get desired results, introduce a noxious stimulus (something the child does not like) or take away an appetitive stimulus (remove something the child really likes). Both of these actions will get the child's full attention, if nothing else. But attention *per se* is not the same as learning.

In order to decrease behavior that is deemed undesirable, a teacher might introduce a noxious stimulus. For example, as shown in Figure 4.1, a teacher might beat a child for being disrespectful or disobedient. If the behavior persists, the teacher might remove an appetitive stimulus by confiscating the child's cell phone for a number of hours, or by banishing the child to the principal's office.

A visit to a classroom today will find many tangible examples of rewards and punishments. Many of these are, in addition to official discipline, standards mandated by the district. The research on this matter is very clear. Punishments rarely work. Furthermore, exclusionary practices have been shown

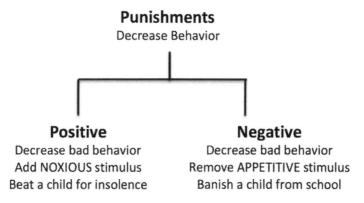

Punishments
Decrease Behavior

Positive
Decrease bad behavior
Add NOXIOUS stimulus
Beat a child for insolence

Negative
Decrease bad behavior
Remove APPETITIVE stimulus
Banish a child from school

FIGURE 4.1 Schema for Operant Conditioning: Punishment

to have ongoing social impact throughout a child's lifespan (*10*). According to experts at the US Department of Health & Human Services and the US Department of Education, children who are suspended or expelled in early years (pre-school or elementary) are up to ten times more likely to not graduate high school (*49*). In addition, these same children experience high levels of academic failure and are placed on a pathway to incarceration later in life (*50*). Yet, exclusionary practices are common in schools everywhere.

To make matters worse, we use the power and speed of the Internet to reward or punish children in real-time. The Bracey Report decries the use of technologies that permit teachers to do in nanoseconds "things that we shouldn't be doing at all (*51*)." For instance, real-time technological programs (e.g., Clipping, see Figure 4.2) are used to discipline children. While there are very real advantages to having an electronic program that allows the guardian to engage so easily with the teacher, labeling and stratification aspects of these programs are dismal for at least 50% children (*52*).

Educational intentions often fail to align with academic outcomes. And technology is rarely the solution. Adding technology to poor pedagogy simply accelerates dysfunction.

Clipping is supposed to "promote good choices" for a child and, conversely, to teach the child how to "learn from poor choices." The child has to be monitored by the teacher who has to "notice" good choices and "notice" bad choices. Beware Pygmalion in the classroom (*34*)! Color code begins with green in the center of the board and goes up, or down, from there. Colors are associated with good and bad behavior. "Good" progresses through blue, purple, and pink. "Bad" sinks through yellow, orange, and red. Clipping down involves quite a bit of public shaming and humiliation, and exclusion from fun activities. The parental reach is a further threat with more punishment, berating, and loss of privileges. Following is an ideal description of how clipping works in a typical classroom. Ideal is often subjective.

Clipping

The child begins each day with a "clip" on Green. Green signifies child is "Ready to Learn."

Clip Up

When teacher notices good behavior, the child will clip up! As the child clips up to the next color (blue), they receive an affirmative signal that acknowledges the "Good Choice." Further good choices will nudge

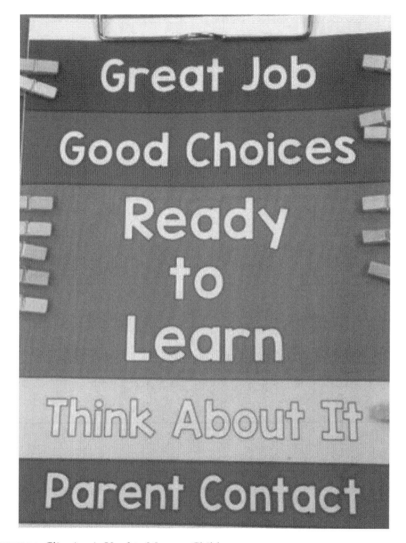

FIGURE 4.2 Clipping is Used to Manage Children

the clip up to colors purple and pink—where the child will be "Off the Chart." Then the child receives a sticker on the back of her clip. Five Stickers earns a special (Token Economy) reward from teacher!

Clip Down

Poor choices will have the opposite effect. If the child is not following rules, they will clip down. Clipping down to yellow is a

WARNING. If they arrive at orange, the child is punished (e.g., lose some or all of recess). If the child lands on RED, this will trigger a cascade of events that could involve the guardian, the principal, and the school psychologist or counselor.

Behavior Calendar

At red, a note is attached to the child's behavior calendar, which is sent home for the guardian's intervention. Every day, the child is asked to color the calendar with the color that she ended on that day. Monthly behavior calendars must remain in the daily folder.

Other classroom management techniques involve high speed Internet so that the child cannot avoid or ignore the very public exposure of what is occurring. Efficiency is the watchword of these programs. In a few nanoseconds, with a simple finger touch to a pervasive smart board screen, a child's compliance can be made public or else! Bribes and threats, carrots and sticks, in fact any kind of reward or punishment, do not sit well with (i) a child's intrinsic motivation, (ii) Reptilian survival instinct, and (iii) emotional midbrain regulation.

Rewards will sometimes gain a short-term compliance, but punishment damages the innate learning capacity that every child is born with. In these tech-enabled compliance "factories", the definition of learning goes out the window. Learning cannot be about teacher "catching" children being good or bad? Instead of "co-creating with" a child in a safe and inclusive environment, the teacher is seen as someone who is "doing" things to kids. The safe welcoming classroom environment that we say we desire and hope to create cannot survive when children are publicly competing with each other for points, token economies, and teacher's approval.

Compliance is a critical teaching component if the ideal stems from quiet children doing what the teacher says. However, learning has nothing to do with compliance: agency and interest ignite each child when the classroom speaks to social and emotional wellbeing. A sense of belonging trumps compliance every time.

Teacher Talk

All teachers will have experienced the opposite to the ideal of compliant, focused learning. They look for tangible, concrete strategies that they can use immediately to solve issues that show up. They typically seek solutions for the five or six children who are just difficult to corral. Herding cats seems easier sometimes. What to do about temper tantrums, aggressive behavior, deliberate disruption, and "externalizing?"

What was Surprising?

Teacher #1

I was surprised at the way we reframed my methods, which I deemed essential. I have to survive in this class. I try to run a tight ship—by providing a learning environment that meets the needs of all my children. But there are always three or four kids who are so disruptive and so aggressive that they take up a lot of my time and most of my patience. I didn't see myself as "pushing out" these kids, but in truth, I am happiest when they are not in my class. It is easier to teach compliant kids—even though I know that compliance and learning are not the same thing. I see it every day. Kids do what they are told, stay under the radar and get by. But they don't seem to be learning anything except not getting caught. Have I fallen into the trap of pushing out the kids who are disruptive? I am surprising myself.

Teacher #2

Active avoidance totally surprised me. I know that most of the children I meet every day are living in that box. And it is a box. I had not experienced the operant conditioning model in such immediate detail. I hadn't seen myself as the purveyor of rewards and punishments so that I could affect a child's behavior in such clear detail. It seems that I don't have any choice. If I allow the child to get away with disruptive behaviors, I won't be able to teach the children who are willing. But I hadn't seen them as just being compliant. I interpreted compliance as willingness. I see the difference now between compliance and agency. This is huge. We end up being "monitors" of behavior. I never signed up to push children out—I want to connect with their innate learning capacity.

What we already knew but now see in a new way?
Teacher #1

I had a suspicion that what I was doing was withholding a privilege in order to gain the child's attention, but I never viewed it as introducing something noxious—a noxious stimulus—that the child would learn to avoid me or even dislike me. Seeing the rewards and punishment model in a new way helps me distinguish between doing what I think is best for the child, and doing something that will push the child further away. "Pushed Out" is a new term for me. Even though I knew it existed and I had a sneaky suspicion that I was part of the pushing out syndrome.

Teacher #2

I already knew that the software package that we were using in our school was hurting some children. I could see it in their faces that they hated to get a bad mark or a demerit. And I disliked that I was the enforcer—it was my job to catch them doing good or bad. I knew that some days I was missing both bad and good and quite honestly, this is not why I signed up to be a teacher. I am not inspired by this kind of child minding.

What we need help with?
Teacher #1

We need help in several areas in relation to managing a classroom if we are not able to use rewards? I don't even know what that would look like.

Strategies for Change

Teachers who have made the shift to a neuro cognitive stance do things very similar to all other teachers. To the un-tutored eye, it might all seem to fit the model that has been occurring in classrooms for a long time. Yet, on deeper investigation and when the observer is shown what to look for, amazing revelations are made visible.

Simple Strategies

1. **Vocabulary?** All change begins with words. When a teacher says something like, "That behavior is unacceptable!" it is clear that the teacher doesn't yet believe that all behavior is communication. The child who is acting up and aggressive is more often than not in an amygdala hijack. Once the teacher recognizes the neural connection, it is easy to engage the problem and bring the child back into executive function brain.
2. **Neurotransmitters?** The room seems filled with fun—how did you do that (e.g., Brain Break. See Figure 4.3)? Why do these children seem to like you and yet they treat me like a pariah? I have to teach them math. They seem to struggle at math, yet they are excelling at composition and writing. Why are they so delayed in math and so advanced in reading, writing? I don't get it?

Radical Strategies

1. **Age plus One!** If the students are 9 years old, plan on getting them out of their seats every 10 minutes (or so), standing up and crossing the midline in a fun brain break.
2. **Attention Grabber!** NOVELTY = ATTENTION! "How many times do I have to remind you—if you would only apply yourself you could be top of your class?" Instead of struggling with threats like this, how about a novel way to guarantee student's attention. One example of novelty is music. Use a harmonica to introduce novelty when it's time to transition (See Figure 4.4). Many teachers are adept at playing a lively chord sequence, which signals the children that it is time to transition. It's easy to associate a pleasant chord with a safe, happy, and supporting learning space.

Summary

In this chapter, we reviewed the science behind why the construct of "punishment" is rarely effective and often damaging for children. For some children,

FIGURE 4.3 Fill the Room with Oxytocin

FIGURE 4.4 Novelty Delivers Attention

it forces them into a place of active avoidance—a far cry from intrinsic motivation. What does it actually look like to remove systems of rewards and punishments, to move toward intrinsic motivation? Body language, words out of our mouths, set-up, transitions, recess—each of these items needs to be adjusted in order to insert a neural commitment into how we show up and teach in our classrooms.

Vocabulary

Stimulus Response, Motivation, Active Avoidance

5

Brain Breaks Work Every Time

Bouncing tennis balls in my class helps my students focus

—*Elementary School Teacher*

Neural Education is foremost a learning platform. It is a tangible academic process that is both theoretical and with practical application. We refer to a "neural lens" that shows up as a nuanced filter for teachers and guardians. Anchored in a simple pedagogical model, teaching with neuroscience aligns with how the brain works and how children learn.

Knowledge of the physical brain is essential. We are often surprised to discover that teachers (and indeed guardians) are the only specialists who do not study the organ that they use most in teaching and raising children. It comes as a shock to many that the human brain evolved over hundreds of millions of years and shows up in the classroom with capacity and capabilities that are both surprising and practical. It clearly falls under the category of "I knew this, but now I see it in a new way." In other words, when teachers understand constructs like limbic system, HPA axis, Cortisol, plasticity, long-term potentiation, stress, myelination, and much more . . . everything in the learning world changes ever so slightly, but always immediately, and lasts forever.

As a species, Homo sapiens inherited a powerful brain that is expressed through three functional areas. These are profoundly connected to (i) survival, (ii) emotions, and (iii) higher-order thinking. Many scientists believe that our species made it to the 21st century because of our powerful evolving brains. Neanderthals, Homo erectus, Homo Africanus, and many other ancestral species didn't make it (53). Our brains probably contributed to this outcome!

As early humans spread around the globe, they encountered diverse climatic and physical environments. Intense survival challenges associated with "not being eaten by the next hungry carnivore that came along" demanded that they enhance their "social" survival skills, and process more and more complex sensory information. In a world of intense competition to stay alive, the ability to run fast on two legs, together with really good hands for manipulating tools, was optimized by developing a large complex brain (54).

"As a species of seeming feeble, naked apes, we humans are unlikely candidates for power in a natural world where dominant adaptations can boil down to speed, agility, jaws, and claws (54)." Paleontologists and evolutionary biological scientists explain how the human species survived against all odds. It appears that early humans used brain-power, innovation, and teamwork to dominate the planet with emergent capacities as follows: (i) cognition, (ii) culture, and (iii) cooperation. Large complex brains can store and process large amounts of complex information. The increased processing power proved to be a big advantage to early humans in their social interactions and encounters with unfamiliar habitats (55).

As humans evolved, they increased their ability to produce white matter connections between nerve cells. Today's children are born with this innate capacity, which facilitates processing and evaluating large volumes of sensory information. Structures grow and myelinate, which increase processing power for manipulating information in short-term memory. At the same time, these structures can increase the amount of memories that are encoded into long-term memory where they are stored for later retrieval.

Claws and Jaws

The hindbrain evolved more than 300 million years ago. A reptilian remnant of the survival brain, it is often referred to as the reactive, involuntary brain associated with freeze, fight and flight. Here the focus is on reactions—fighting is a reaction to fear, pain, and danger. All children are endowed with healthy reactive brains, and are capable of recognizing danger, and fear, and will respond appropriately with fight or flight.

Love and Joy

The midbrain is associated with emotions. Only mammals inherited this more recently evolved region from roughly 100 million years ago. This is the region responsible for learning, music, art, science, and technology. It is also associated with a sense of belonging, connecting with others, overcoming impulsive behaviors, the ability to contribute in a collaborative way, and capacity for self regulation. In this respect, the limbic emotional midbrain is an important ameliorating touchstone for the animal, reactive brain that reflects the much-older period.

Imagination and Intuition

The forebrain is the higher-order thinking brain, 4 million years of evolutionary time. In this region of the brain, the child is able to reflect, revise thinking, plan, predict, and solve problems. It is especially practical for critical and original thinking, insight, creativity, and other higher-order cognitive skills. Metacognition is a higher-order cognitive skill that connects all three regions; reactive space, emotional space, and critical thinking space.

We are endowed with a natural and innate capacity to learn. Figure 5.1 shows a mature brain in the human skull that is capable of both thinking and surviving. Our children make meaning in their world. Sometimes, naïve "meaning-making" culminates in pre-conceptions and misconceptions that limit comprehension and erode understanding. Learning scientists recommend mental models that are based on how the brain works. Mental models

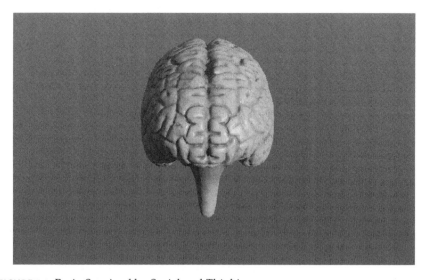

FIGURE 5.1 Brain Survived by Social and Thinking

about the brain are decidedly more appropriate for forming enduring ideas with deep understanding (56).

By adhering to a neural method, teacher focus is always on strengthening synaptic connections with the knowledge that we are increasing white matter tracts. In this model, teachers are cognizant of limitations of working memory. Intentionality for activating neurotransmitters helps promote learning with emotional connections; thus, connecting reptilian hindbrain and limbic midbrain with cortical forebrain.

Agentic learning scenarios foster common vocabulary for neural educators. They articulate practice and processes that ignite children to generate new ideas. A novice member to the Neural Education Facebook group gasped in amazement after a monthly PLC (Professional Learning Community) online gathering:

> What surprised me was the fluency with which you speak about neurotransmitters, working memory, white matter circuits, and plasticity. This is not my usual classroom vocabulary. In our school, we talk about IEPs, At Risk behaviors, and appropriate disciplinary actions for disrupting our lessons.
>
> (Neural Ed PLC, 2020)

It's neurobiological. Humans are hardwired for learning. We are constantly in a state of arousal and attention for danger and surprise. Biological structures like the Reticular Activating System and the Amygdalae are attuned to external stimuli and inbound sensory information from the environment. The overriding "go to" susceptibility is reactive—an involuntary response to perceived stressors, which can hijack a learner—flight, fight, freeze, or paralysis. Pathways to executive functions of the prefrontal cortex are shut down in such situations. This is where "brain breaks" relieve the crisis.

Brain Breaks

Brain Breaks restore the child to higher-order thinking brain. The premise is simple: amygdala hijack causes shutdown to the forebrain. Use Brain Breaks with the child in your classroom who is acting out, hostile, even aggressive and is not able to access higher-order processing. Consider the principal who challenges the child that has shown up in his office with the disappointing grimace: "I am surprised to see you here. You are usually so diligent with your work." And the child responds, "I am surprised to be here, myself." Amygdala hijack! Brain Break! The child in amygdala hijack is in need of a fun brain break, to release oxytocin, serotonin, and dopamine.

Brain Breaks are fun and usually less-than-a-minute, high-energy physical activities designed to activate cognitive and emotional brain regions. We recommend crossing the midline to further activate dense white matter tracts in the corpus callosum. Active movement boosts blood flow, sending oxygen to the brain. And physical, social activities enhance working memory, promote skills in being present and, by overturning amygdala hijack, enable the child to engage higher-order processing.

Teacher Talk

The idea that a child might be stuck in a reactive "freeze, fight, flight" state is revealing news to guardians and teachers. It is not a safe assumption to make that when a child shows up in a classroom, he or she is ready to learn. Far from it! In fact, most teachers who are aware of the amygdala hijack effect are prone to begin every lesson with a brain break because they must assume (out of an abundance of caution) that the child is arriving in some aggravated state that reduces mental activity. The brain break guarantees that the child will shift into the prefrontal cortex where they can access higher-order thinking and cognitive skills.

What was Surprising?

Teacher #1

I was surprised how easy it is to get children into a fight, flight situation.

Teacher #2

Surprised—I am shocked. It makes sense now in retrospect. Children who are in a reactive reptilian hindbrain are not able to access their higher-order executive function. This makes sense. I have seen the fight/flight so many times and I never associated it with blocked access. I always assumed it was out of willful aggression and stubbornness. I am saddened by my lack of awareness. I should know this. We all should. It must be worse for a child online. They spend so much time in Teams or Zoom meetings and how can we help them stay out of their amygdala?

What we already knew but now see in a new way?
Teacher #1

I had heard of fight or flight, but I now see it as part of a much more complex system. The idea that the brain is evolved over such a long time and that we still have a reptilian brain as well as a sapiens brain is mesmerizing. I can see also now why punishments could never work in a fight/flight encounter. What is worse for me is how many times I was in an amygdala hijack myself when confronting a child whose behavior was not in line with school policy. Adult amygdala hijack cannot fix child amygdala hijack. This is very upsetting.

Teacher #2

I knew that we all have parts of our brain dedicated to survival, but I never placed it in the realm of learning and teaching. I can see now that when the child is in a state of hijack that there is no point in trying to teach her until she is brought back into her prefrontal cortex. This is huge. Thank you so much for highlighting this for me. I love brain breaks but I never thought of them as relieving children of stress . . . of their fears, survival, or danger. I know that some kids see danger in school—they are in a hyper-vigilant state all day. Many of my kids are from a different culture and are learning English as a second language—they are hijacked a lot. I knew brain breaks work, but now I am going to get serious about using them regularly.

What we need help with?
Teacher #1

Where can I get good brain breaks? I am convinced that they work, but I don't want to get stale with the same ones every day?

Teacher #2

I need to know some more strategies for getting children out of the freeze, fight, and flight syndrome. Racial bias is rampant in my school. It seems to me that a lot of kids live in that hyperactive state.

Strategies for Change

Teachers who have made the shift to a neuro cognitive stance do things very similar to all other teachers. To the un-tutored eye, it might all seem to fit the model that has been occurring in classrooms for a long time. Yet, on deeper investigation and when the observer is shown what to look for, amazing revelations are made visible.

Simple Strategies

1. **Physical Brain Breaks?** Brain breaks are the same as play for children. The cognitive benefits of play are abundantly documented in neuroscience. Experts assure us that the pharmacological advantages of play cannot be overestimated (57). Play is a way to test the possibilities of their environment without consequence—no extrinsic rewards or punishments, just pure fun.
2. **Neurotransmitters for Brain Breaks?** Children experience their synaptic receptors flooded with appropriate neurotransmitters that promote learning. Norepinephrine helps anticipation and focus; dopamine is flush with happiness and fun; serotonin is palpable in their play and sense of pleasure; and oxytocin is connected to bonding, sense of belonging, and fun. Safe to predict that while these neurotransmitters flood the synapses, there is no aggression in the room—no cortisol, and no fear. When teachers talk about safe learning environment this is what they are aspiring towards.

Radical Strategies

3. **Virtual Brain Breaks!** When we teach online and have no physical link to the children or their environment, it is not as easy to stop everything and jump into a brain break. However, a well-timed

video of children engaged in fun brain break activities can have the same effect. Watch the video together and share in the fun while the children watch and anticipate, engage in the laughter and cheering, and experience the sense of belonging and bonding that is implied.

4. **Co-create Brain Breaks!** When the child is actually inventing brain breaks, we achieve a win-win learning system. The rules are simple.
   - Must be standing (if possible) to get the blood flow from the thighs to the brain
   - Must be active to engage the cerebellum for movement and balance
   - Must include small-motor skills to engage the parietal lobe
   - Must involve seeing and hearing and speaking (singing, laughing, humming, etc.) to engage the occipital and temporal lobes
   - Must cross the midline so that the corpus callosum is activated

Summary

In this chapter, the neuroscience of learning is anchored in evolution. The brain has a long connection with emotions that stem from fear, danger, and survival. Teachers will reassess how they interact with children who are not in full control of their executive function or higher-order critical decision-making processes. Children, who are not yet fully developed but have access to a well-formed fight or flight system, should not be punished. They need practice in first co- and then self-regulation through metacognition. Strategies for managing the classroom by managing the brain begin with teachers who recognize their own amygdala hijack and know how to get back to their own prefrontal cortex. With self-care, teachers excel in a world where stress response is not always easy. In the next chapter, we apply information we learned in the last three chapters to a cognitive model that is aligned with intention with how the brain works and how children learn.

Vocabulary

Agentic Learning, Freeze Flight Fight, Metacognition

6

Cognitive Models Work Every Time

Cogito, ergo sum. . . . I think, therefore I am

—*René Descartes (Discourse on Method, 1637)*

Everyone has a model of school in their heads. It usually places a teacher up front; neat rows of students who are attentively looking forward towards the teacher. When asked to do so, most people can place themselves in their most "liked" or most "hated" classroom, and recall with exquisite detail the room, the subject, the teacher, and classmates. In the idyllic classroom, a backdrop consists of a chalkboard and a map. Typically, a child is enthusiastically waving a hand high to assure the teacher that she has the answer to a question.

Models like this are culturally constructed because each of us has been in classrooms that fit this image (*58*). Figure 6.1 is an example of a classroom from a school early in the 20th century, at a time when a monitor (usually an older boy) who was instructed by the teacher, is tasked with teaching 3Rs to younger children. The 3Rs consisted of Reading, wRiting, and aRithmetic, the subjects which counted for examination and payment for the teacher (*59*). People remark that it is interesting how chalkboards of the 1820s resemble iPads of the 2020s. Some would even argue that school hasn't changed that much.

This is a time of large paradigm shifts in everything relating to schools, technology, and learning. The teacher who taught in the 1820s or the 1920s (even the 1980s) would be hard-pressed to manage the pace and technology of a classroom in any school today. Smart boards, personal computing

FIGURE 6.1 Early 20th Century School Room

devices, and other tech devices have replaced traditional "brick-and-mortar" classrooms. While most children still carry heavy backpacks, textbooks are online, and nearly all homework and assignments can be completed and shared online. The iGen kids are at home with collaborative projects in the cloud, (see Figure 6.2) emails, texting, Facebook, TikTok, and a host of other Instagram, and Twitter-type programs that allow them to share, engage, and interact in a four-dimensional world that is quite foreign to our conception of a traditional school.

But this is a world where information is coming at us at a pace and severity that is blistering. We struggle with how to curate it, and how to ingest and process it. Twenty-first century skills and qualities differ substantially from what was accepted in the day when the 3Rs were measures of a child's capacity. Today, we value a comprehensive list of qualities and skills, which are important to managing ebb and flow of information in a fast-paced world. These include persistence, curiosity, enthusiasm, courage, leadership, creativity, growth-mindset, civic-mindedness, resourcefulness, self-regulation, sense of wonder, big-picture thinking, compassion, reliability, motivation, humor, empathy, sense of beauty, humility, and resilience. This is the age where we are inundated with information but starved for wisdom (60).

FIGURE 6.2 Smart Class 2020

Managing classrooms is molecular—it's really about managing the brain with increased pace, increased amounts of information, and increased stress levels because of an increased need to succeed in a fast-paced world. It is clear that schools are in crisis (61). From a neurobiological standpoint, it boils down to limitations of working memory. Children need increased processing power and speed for managing incoming data bits in an information age. Structures exist that are supposed to help.

The brain's reticular activating system, for instance, acts as a filter for sensory information coming into the brain. These include sounds, tastes, colors, images, and pictures—anything up to two million bits of data every second. Some of this information is processed in the non-conscious brain and doesn't impact the learning brain. Important information is routed to the amygdala and will be sent to either the involuntary, reactive brain, or to the prefrontal cortex for processing. As we learned earlier, information that is routed to the reactive brain will be processed with a freeze, fight, or flight response—since that is the only response from this involuntary space (62). Working memory is incapacitated in this scenario. And working memory is already small (63).

Miller's Law, Cognitive Load, and the 3Rs

George Miller, in 1956, published an important paper that outlined the physical limitations of working memory (*64*). At the time, it was an innocuous paper and didn't make any waves, but before long his *Magical Number Seven Plus or Minus Two* influenced computer science, artificial intelligence, telephone numbers, and teaching and learning. In teaching situations, Miller's Law refers to the upper limit of processing—Seven Plus Two—above which the student will experience cognitive overload. According to this calculation, some individuals can handle five pieces of new information and others can handle up to nine pieces of new information. In a classroom, this limitation is important to note, so that the teacher can help children who might be struggling to stay up with the lesson. The problem might not be comprehension; it might simply be that the working memory space is full.

By definition, working memory refers to an individual's capacity to hold information for a short amount of time in the exercise of an immediate task. Everybody has working memory and, just like a computer's memory, we know when it is full or when there is plenty of room for more processing. Today, with ubiquitous technological gadgets, our working memory gets a break with phone numbers, addresses, appointments, GPS, mapping, and a host of other bits of information that in another time—pre cell phone—we had to hold in our heads. George Miller's famous paper and the length of any US phone number are related (*65*).

Like everything else pertaining to a child's brain, working memory is very complex. It's difficult to assign a single location for working memory, but most scientists accept that the prefrontal executive region manages semantic and abstract sense making. Scientists have identified localized functional regions that are involved in storing temporary bits of information when they are associated with, for instance, visual-spatial information or with small-motor skill information or with auditory information, and so on. A simple way to look at size is to compare working memory with the processing power of the rest of the brain. Most teachers are shocked to discover that if we imagine the size of a child's working memory as approximately one cubic foot, then the rest of the brain by comparison is equal to fifteen-times the Milky Way (*66*).

Working Memory is distinguished from long-term memory by its very nature. While short-term (working) memory persists about 12 seconds, information can remain in long-term memory indefinitely. Scraps of information that we hold in working memory stay around for a long moment and then disappear. Given its size, this memory space can fill up easily. When it is full, you know it. People often say things like, "My brain hurts, it's full . . . I can't do this anymore." Yet, we need our short-term memory a million times each day to interact with a fast-paced, information-rich society. For example, I might need to memorize a new phone number for a few seconds as I toggle between apps in order to key it into my iPhone.

Plain and simple, when a teacher breaks Miller's Law by failing to simplify information into bite-sized chunks that are easily digestible, the child might experience cognitive overload and possibly go into amygdala hijack. Cognitive load differs from student to student and from day to day. Working memory differs from student to student and from day to day also. Working memory doesn't necessarily fill up because of the cognitive load— it can just as easily fill up because of things that happen outside the class, stressors, fear, low self-esteem, competition, or jealousy. Teaching routines create safety and mental structures that help the child manage incoming information. These schemas are cognitive structures that make up a child's knowledge base (67).

Neural approaches use cognitive models to replace the old understanding of literacy and numeracy with the 3Rs that speak to brain, engagement, and intrinsic motivation. Reading, writing, and arithmetic are still central aspects of these neural 3Rs, but so too is art, drama, music, and movement. In a space where generating new ideas is important, the new 3Rs are focused on mental criteria that focus on (i) *Reflect*, (ii) *Revised Thinking*, and (iii) *Report Out*. The cognitive model not only emphasizes a mentalistic approach, but it thrives in it.

Teacher Talk

A tangible board is a simple but highly affective cognitive model that is accessible because it aligns with learning and neuroscience. Everything about a neural lens is intentional because the human brain is designed to learn, is predisposed to amygdala hijack, and is capable of self-regulation.

What was Surprising?
Teacher #1

I was surprised that there is a limit to working memory.

Teacher #2

I am surprised about Miller's Law. How come I had never heard of Miller? It is probably the number one go-to, most important piece of knowledge for presenting new information? Chunking.

What we already knew but now see in a new way?
Teacher #1

I knew about cognitive load from a class I took. But I hadn't connected it with that kid who looks lost in class when his brain is full. I would think . . . "Lights are on, but nobody's home!" It makes sense to me now—working memory full, kid is in amygdala hijack, and I see the fight/flight response. Kid says, "I'm no good at math."

Teacher #2

This Miller's Law changes everything. Kids get overloaded so easily. And it is not their fault. It is simply that their working memory gets full. I am so glad to be able to associate cognitive load with Miller's Law and have a solution with a simple brain break. Oxytocin. I see now how neurotransmitters are better than cortisol.

What we need help with?
Teacher #1

I downloaded the *Challenge Board* from the web. That was easy. The kids love using *Nedheads* (see Figure 6.3). But where can I find more information about why it works?

Teacher #2

I want more information on Miller's Law. I read that seven plus or minus two was later adjusted to four plus or minus two. Does that mean four new concepts are the limit?

FIGURE 6.3 Children Select NED Heads on the NED Challenge Board

Strategies for Change

When we apply the filter of Miller's (adjusted) Law to our work, teachers think in terms of two. In 2001, Professor Cowan (working with Miller) revised down the capacity limits to four plus or minus two (*68*). Mindful of children's propensity for amygdala hijack, we recommend that teachers work from the lower capacity limit of two.

Simple Strategies

1. **Ned Challenge Board?** Print the Neural Education *Challenge Board* in color (see Figure 6.4). Laminate it with thick lamination. Use one board for groups of five or six students. Allow students to choose their own *Nedheads* as they progress together through each challenge.
2. **Role Play?** Children are good at role-play. Be consistent about the roles—Task Master, Time Keeper, Scribe, Report Out Spokesperson. Roles rotate so that every student gets to collaborate, lead, contribute, and generate ideas.

Radical Strategies

3. **One Big Idea!** Mindful of Miller's Law, always design lesson plans backwards. Focus on One Big Idea. Each plan should answer the

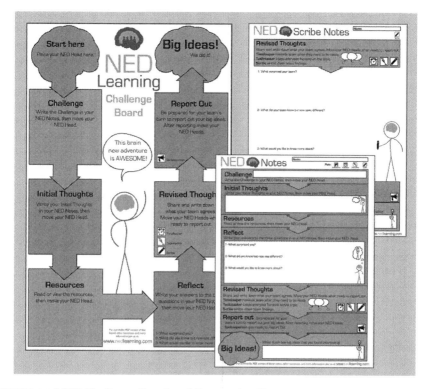

FIGURE 6.4 NED Challenge Board and Supporting Notes

question; "What is the one big idea that my students will take away when this lesson is over?"

4. **Two Scaffolding Supports!** If the child is going to walk away with this One Big Idea, what are the two supporting ideas that the child must know in order to deeply understand the Big Idea?

Summary

In this chapter, we explored Miller's Law and cognitive load. They both go together since they show up in every classroom, every day. When the child's working memory is full, there is no point trying to squeeze any more information in there. You will know it is full because the child will be acting squirrely, coming from a place of freeze, flight, or fight. Use brain breaks to get the child back into the executive function of the prefrontal cortex. Fun brain breaks with serotonin, oxytocin,, and dopamine will ready the child for learning by clearing out working memory. In the next chapter, we will explore how genetics and epigenetics show up in your classroom, sometimes with surprising consequences.

Vocabulary

Schema, Working Memory, Miller's Law

7

Orchids Are Epigenetic

It makes sense that sensitive children wilt easily.

—*Middle School Teacher*

My basement is home to way too many wilted orchids. I don't like to admit that, but orchids are difficult to raise. I keep them as reminders—of the way I used to teach in my early years. Wilted orchids were common back then. Not anymore. I raised a couple orchids in the traditional rewards and punishment mode long before there was any chatter about children being "orchidial" or "dandelinic." More recently, I experienced the great privilege of raising two children with new information and updated models through a neuroscience of learning stance. The difference was life-changing both for me and the children.

Orchids are epiphytes and, thus, are intensely sensitive. Stemming from the Greek *epi*, which means above, and *phyte*, which means plant, an epiphytic orchid grows not in the ground, but on a host plant, giving the impression that it survives in thin air. Some children are like orchids in terms of sensitivity, "ungroundedness," and susceptibility to wilt. But when greenhoused, these same orchidial children can be as enigmatically sparkling as the most colorful botanical bloom.

It begins with a child's genetic inheritance from mom and dad. Genetics is important, but epigenetics (see Figure 7.1) also plays a large part in how the orchid shows up in the classroom. Epigenetics means over and above the genome. The child gets a genetic framework from mom and dad, which is

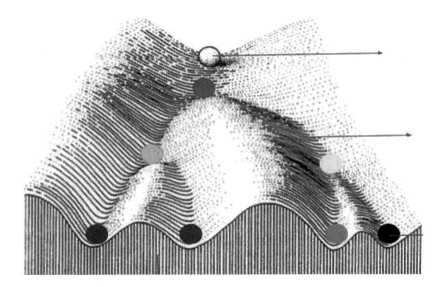

FIGURE 7.1 Epigenetics Influence Who We Are

the nature component. But mom and dad's job is not complete. They create a home with nurturing environment, which also influences which genes will be expressed. Basically, beyond the "nature" component (genetics), the "nurture" component (epigenetics) also makes a large contribution since environmental stimuli can cause genes to be turned on or off.

Just like the plant, Orchid Children also need a caring host because they, too, cannot survive in thin air. Unlike dandelions, which can grow in a crack in the concrete, orchids require careful greenhousing. Filters, associated with a neural perspective, provide strong, healthy, and accessible "greenhouse" techniques. Intuitively, we know these filters. But the science that makes them visible solidifies the approach.

Orchids have a reputation for being difficult to grow; a misinformed botanical remnant of colonial explorers who misunderstood both the nature and the nurture of the species. What worked in Africa didn't necessarily work in London—until botanical science made clear how to take care of such a delicate and sensitive specimen. Orchid lovers paint a different picture— one that dispels many of the myths and legends associated with the fabulously enigmatic, botanical beauty. If you know what you are doing, they are as easy to grow as daisies or African violets.

Similarly, with a newly acquired neural toolkit, teachers, who know how to greenhouse children, will testify to two things. The first is rather incredulous, but data confirm the finding (*69*). Not only do discipline issues go away, it turns out that the children who used to be the known "troublemakers" suddenly find their voice, become agentic contributors, and often adopt a leading role in the classroom. At first we questioned this finding, but after multiple daily replications we had to admit that, indeed, it is in line with what Dr. Boyce reported from his many years of research on this matter (70).

Orchids typically chart a difficult course through life, experiencing high morbidities in health and troubled school encounters. In short, many suffer worst outcomes. This we knew. Orchid children are expensive in terms of health events, time to manage, and energy to support. But what we didn't expect—even though it was clearly stated in Dr. Boyce's findings—is that the Orchid Child can also experience the best outcomes (71). That is, if they are "greenhoused" by four consistently, caring guardians and/or teachers.

The science is clear. Most families have noticed that siblings who might have been born just a couple of years apart reared in the same family are like chalk and cheese—totally different from each other. How could this be? While most children are resilient, able to cope pretty well with stress and adversity, some are more sensitive. They are neurobiologically more reactive to social context. This makes it harder for them to deal with stressful situations.

In any population anywhere, approximately 25% of children will be hyper sensitive (72). That means that in your classroom today, out of 25 children four to six will take up most of your time. These are the kids who can't follow instructions, pay attention, stay focused, initiate tasks, stay on task, or turn in assignments on time. They are dysregulated. Every classroom everywhere will have some of these exacting children. Pediatricians characterize them as prone to excessive morbidities, high maintenance, expensive needs, delinquencies, and bad choices. The metaphor, while not stratifying children, is useful to demonstrate the continuum between extremes—resilience on one end and hypersensitivity on the other.

"Neurobiological" means that the children were born this way—hardwired. Certain alleles of a gene can take more than one form—polymorphic—thus a child who receives a short-short version of the serotonin transporter gene might display high levels of autonomic nervous system reactivity. This child might show up in your classroom with behaviors that will push all your buttons. The Orchid Child displays a high degree of susceptibility to both bad and good environments, whereas the dandelion child is relatively unperturbed by either environment.

This has tremendous bearing on how you approach the classroom. If you create a learning space that is governed by rewards and punishments, the Orchid Child will show up as an externalizing challenge that cannot be avoided. Meanwhile, the rewards and punishments "appear" to be working for the majority of children who comprise "low reactivity" resilient dandelions. These children show no physiological or biological response to life's physical challenges. It matters not a whit whether we use rewards or punishments for resilient children—they are mostly unperturbed by life's challenges.

But the Orchid Child shows up different. Even if you think that you exude a welcoming safe environment, they will perceive your learning space as hostile. For them, it negates their sense of belonging, increases their level of cortisol, and threatens to make a spectacle of their lack of preparedness for life or school. These children are forced to live in the dark recesses of their reptilian involuntary survival brain, because their safety and sense of equanimity are threatened. It's a fight or flight world where hyper-vigilance, mistrust, and fear prevent them from accessing the power of their neocortex and higher-order thinking. It is no wonder that these kids fail at school, opt out early, and never reach their potential.

Yet, it is so easy to raise orchids. Build a greenhouse—invite them in; ask them to play. They will find their own greenhouse if the guardian or teacher fails to provide a welcoming space for them. The greenhouse might be in isolation at home, on the street, in gangs, in alcohol, drugs, ISIS, music, clothes, and many other maladaptive psychopathologies and psychosocial issues that are both dangerous and unwarranted (73).

Orchids will wilt or they will thrive. When the orchid wilts, we shouldn't change the plant; we change the environment. The learning space must be nurturing, supportive, and non-threatening with at least four consistently caring adults in the child's life. Safety and sense of belonging are critical for the child to blossom and thrive. But that same child will wither drastically and deteriorate beyond measure if they encounter a hostile, unsafe, and uncaring, punitive learning space. Neural plasticity accomplishes the work—both good and bad. But the teacher is in control. Know the science. Co-create the space and enjoy the fruits of your garden.

Teacher Talk

The science of differential neurobiological susceptibility to social context is so new that many teachers were taken by surprise with the details and the implications for their work.

What was Surprising?

Teacher #1

I was surprised to learn yet another connection between botany and pedagogy. Piaget, too, was a botanist, a biologist, and finally, a developmental psychologist. It makes sense to see connections between the world of botany, biology, and developmental neuroscience today.

Teacher #2

I was very surprised to find out that I myself am an orchid. I wish I had known this when I was struggling to "fit in" all my life. I always felt like an outsider, as if I was from a different planet. The fact that I am sensitive makes sense—I feel things intensely and it has impacted my entire life. I will now be a more resilient teacher since I can use the science in my pedagogy.

What we already knew but now see in a new way?

Teacher #1

This is amazing! I knew about genetics. . . . I knew it was important. In my teaching career, I have tried to answer the question, "Was it nature or nurture?" And I knew there was a tension or a balance between these two factors. Now I see that epigenetics is key. I interpret epigenetics as environmental factors turning on or turning off genes. I look at it like walking into a library and all the books are on the shelves. But it is only the books that I choose to read that influence who I am and what I become.

Teacher #2

I read Dr. Boyce's book about the research that underlies the Orchid Child. It blew me away. I knew that there were hypersensitive children in my school, and I also knew that they had lots of potential if only I could reach them. I was under the impression that I could make them like the other kids, the dandelion children, and that success would look like a compliant classroom with all kids learning.

But now I see that the Orchid Children are NOT broken dandelions; they are these amazing, talented, colorful bright people that can outshine any dandelion. Their potential is way more than compliant kids, if we know how to greenhouse them properly. This is a big breakthrough for me.

What we need help with?

Teacher #1

I like the idea of Teaching to the Orchid. I like your buttons that challenge every teacher to acknowledge the orchid. But what does that mean? How do I operationalize teaching to the orchid in my classroom?

Teacher #2

I have tried the pedagogic model that you recommend—the challenge model. Does the model teach to the orchid? Is that what teaching to the orchid means? I can see that children love the routine of the challenge board. But if I implement the model with the 3Rs as you recommend, is that enough?

Strategies for Change

Teach to the Orchid is the catchword of neural educators. It is not as intuitive as it may seem, until you install the set of filters that they use to engage and ignite. But, once you achieve even a modicum of success with the Orchid Child, the results will be so spectacular that both you and the child will want more. It's a dopamine thing.

Simple Strategies

1. **Sense of Belonging** Watch Franz deWaal's mesmerizing YouTube video that explains inequities. We quickly realize that no matter how hard we try . . . orchids will always be in the left cage. They will always perceive the world as cucumber rather than grapes. When we begin to see the world as the orchid sees the world, then can we

understand the desperate need for sense of belonging, security, feeling "part of" that is a dynamic makeup of the typical Orchid Child. An ounce of intentionality in this regard will issue momentum and academic progress.

2. **Priming for Oxytocin** Recently I watched a teacher use "bouncing balls" to increase her first graders' engagement. They had so much fun together and it was so successful that the children were happy, learning, and enjoying the math that was built-in. She had practiced the process of taking a ball from the dominant hand around the back and transferring to the less dominant hand while counting out loud to one hundred in fives. They started each round by singing together in a fun way—*HERE WE GO!* The children were very good at this task—so good, in fact, that teacher stopped counting and let them run the show entirely. Automaticity! When the students reach automaticity, working memory is emptied, stress goes away, and individuals are able to contribute in a safe, inviting environment. Two things sprang from this social evaluative surge: (i) children feel good about being successful at this task that included autonomy, mastery, and purpose, (ii) the teacher increased cognitive load with a more difficult math task that stretched the children's capacity. Stretch and Consolidate. Cognitive load was then restored, back to the safety of automaticity. *HERE WE GO!* As soon as the children feel added stress, they are faced with persevering, or giving up easily. Teacher brings them back to automaticity by revisiting the earlier task. Immediately, working memory is emptied, children are engaged and they again are intrinsic with autonomy, mastery, and purpose. This method of stretching the child up to the edge of their capacity and then taking them back into a safe space helps the child grow confidence, self-esteem, and self-efficacy. The key was *HERE WE GO!* Every time the child hears and sings these words, she know she is (i) in a safe space, (ii) in a loving environment where mastery is guaranteed, and (iii) ready for more.

Radical Strategies

3. **Adaptive Expertise** It takes courage to take a risk, step outside your comfort zone, be prepared to be wrong, and to learn from others, and, especially, to tolerate ambiguity. Life gets complicated when there are 20 or so children (not to mention guardians and

administrators, principals and colleagues) in the room. And on top of that, there is the need for online and distance learning. Never was it so important to really understand what it means to be an "adaptive expert" in your field. Install the neural filter. Be on the lookout for the kid with the amygdala hijack so that you can immediately infuse serotonin, norepinephrine, and oxytocin into the lesson. Co-create a new layer of safety and sense of belonging for that same child who is making life so difficult for you right now. Take a deep breath and be grateful for the opportunity to co-regulate while the child is beginning to self-regulate.

4. **Intrinsic Motivation** Ask yourself: "Where is the autonomy for each child in this part of the lesson? Where is the Me, Here, Now?" Carefully restructure the lesson plan so that each child feels part of the work, is able to contribute to the effort, and is able to discover a sense of mastery.

Summary

In this chapter, we reviewed the science of resilience versus sensitivity. Children reflect their innate hardwired autonomic nervous system reactivity towards social context. Schools and homes are serious social contexts for children. Whether they show up with a resilient competence or a reactive sensitivity is outside their control—that is, until we teach them about their neurobiological make-up and how to navigate life.

In this section, we set out to demonstrate how paradigm shifts are necessary if we are to be successful at (i) recognizing how our children show up in the world, and (ii) understanding the neurobiological features of learning that are either accessible or difficult. In the next section, we explore several elements of pedagogy that reflect the new paradigmatic shifts, which take place when we enter a cognitive learning space.

Vocabulary

Orchidial, Dandelinic, Epigenetic

Part II
Rethinking Pedagogy

8

Miller's (Adjusted) Law

I look at my phone number differently today.

—*High School Student*

Miller's magical-number-seven Law is probably the most important classroom imperative that educators never heard of. It's not unusual that teachers would have missed Miller in the context of pedagogy or child discipline. However, scientific principles outlined in it make the *Magical-Number-Seven* paper an essential read for all classroom instruction and lesson planning. Miller and classroom instruction might, at first glance, appear to be strange conceptual bed-fellows, but they are inextricably conjoined in a world that is drowning in information while staggering under the pace of change (74). Miller's work was not concerned with either teacher preparation or classroom management, yet he is relevant in every learning space—k12 or workplace training and development.

In his early career, Miller's academic interests focused on advancing two areas related to computer science and cognitive psychology. Thus, in 1956, we find him immersed in studies about artificial intelligence and information theory. His influential paper (64) *'The Magical Number Seven plus or minus Two'* was made public at the Massachusetts Institute of Technology[1] on September 11, 1956—a day that is now revered as the tangible moment that the "Cognitive Revolution" occurred. It was a nondescript, quiet revolution with very few people in the room. Yet, half a dozen groundbreaking papers were presented to an audience of like-minded experts who, apparently, were blithely impervious to the long shadow cast by their research.

A Cognitive Revolution

Miller's paper turns out to be one of the most-cited papers in psychology.[2] From this work, the notion of "chunking" information captured the attention and imagination of business leaders and thinkers. Nevertheless, it did not find its way into teacher preparation courses and rarely does it influence methodologies. It is noteworthy that Donald Hebb's important work on "cell assemblies" was also released in that room. "Hebbian Theory" is equally critical in classrooms today, where cognitive rehearsal is premised on the neurophysiological rule: *Neurons that Fire Together Wire Together* (75). And, finally, Noam Chomsky, the man most singly responsible for refuting Skinner's behaviorist views on language acquisition (26), presented a paper and precursor to his notable monograph *"Syntactic Structures,"* which laid the foundation for theoretical linguistics (76).

That his academic world would spill over into learning sciences was something that Miller never saw coming. But that particular conceptual collision had widespread repercussions that are as meaningful today as they were on that fateful day in 1956. It started out as an unintended consequence of understanding the innate limits of working memory. That concept of "limited channel capacity" was not, and for the most part, is not something that teachers associate with their students when they prepare lesson plans. However, understanding this critical concept prevents children from cognitive overload, amygdala hijack, and negative reticular activating system spirals. In other words, when teachers plan for "limited channel capacity," they typically have more engaged classrooms and less need for what has become the dreaded consequence for every student today—progressive punitive practice.

A Magical Conundrum

Working memory is defined as the ability to hold in mind, manipulate, and update information in memory. From the brain's viewpoint, incoming sensory information is either (i) encoded into long-term memory, or (ii) it decays, or (iii) it's replaced. When new information is introduced it needs to be (i) actively attended to, or (ii) rehearsed. Otherwise, it will have a short duration, typically 10 to 12 seconds. This information is constant bedrock for educators and will mean the difference between attention and disruptive behaviors.

Three factors shape Miller's fitful journey to the learning sciences. These factors are not related and, at times, seem a little serendipitous. The first falls into the realm of "incredulous," since his research conclusions with regard to limitations of working memory are momentous for all learning. It's hard to comprehend how this important information managed to not show up in classrooms for 65 years. Baddeley described how a child's "cognitive architecture has a mechanism that limits the scope of immediate changes to the knowledge base. It is severely limited in capacity and duration when dealing with novel elements of information (63)." This one omission on its own is colossal because of the immense impact that this specific understanding delivers to teaching, knowledge transfer, and especially, to children's attention capabilities.

The second factor falls into the realm of "well maybe." Miller's colleague and Nobel laureate, Herbert Simon, put the "cat among the pigeons" when he immediately disagreed (1956) with the study pronouncements about unit limits. Convinced that the number seven was "too high," Simon suggested something more like three as the upper limit (plus or minus two). "George had the right idea, but the wrong number (68)." Notwithstanding the difference of opinion, that study was not replicated for 50 years, and the results went unquestioned with implications that affected each of us every day. Because, beyond education, Miller's magical number seven had far-reaching impact on the rest of American life—his research was foundational framing for the number of digits in telephone numbers. Before George passed in 2012, he worked with professor Cowan to take a fresh look at the issues surrounding working memory. They replicated the study to verify, once and for all, what were the limitations. It turns out that Herb Simon was correct. Today, educators operate from a revised limitation—closer to three than seven.

Finally, in the mid 70s, the third factor delivered the most important consideration for teachers and students. And this too, must fall under the category of "even more incredulous!" In a groundbreaking study, Anders Ericsson, the Swedish psychologist who came to work with Herbert Simon at Carnegie Melon, brought new clarity to Miller's working memory theory. Ericsson[3] was interested in exploring just how "fixed" was the innate capacity to manipulate information in working memory. The accepted "certainty" of the day (1975) was of a "universal" limit—that working memory or "channel capacity" was fixed in accordance with Miller's Law at seven units. His discovery that memory was not "fixed" and could be improved with training was a revolutionary finding that should have been pivotal for all educators (77). But, just like the original finding about "channel capacity," Ericsson's work floated by in quietude with no implications for learning.

Soon after publication, Miller's general principles of channel capacity and limits to working memory had widespread and immediate impact on scientific communities. Researchers in linguistics, anthropology, artificial intelligence, neuroscience, computer science, psychology, and philosophy were influenced to varying degrees by channel capacity. By contrast, it's difficult to find even one teacher anywhere who starts her day thinking about the magical number seven plus or minus two and its relationship to a child's working memory, or cognitive load. To compound this un-magical conundrum, which teacher, while flossing her teeth in the morning, is conjuring up methods and practice that can increase and strengthen a child's working memory? So, why do teachers not know about Miller, Ericsson, Simon, and, in particular the limitations and malleability of working memory?

Pillars of Pedagogy and a Keystone

Miller and Hebb forge strong supporting columns in the ark of the cognitive revolution; teacher as neural educator is the keystone that binds. In Figure 8.1, the teacher is neuro-enabled in co-regulating with the child. Together, they build a solid learning structure. It's not just about content (STEM or otherwise); instead, the cognitive revolution focuses on learning sciences. The teacher is key to unlock the innate capacity of the child who will excel with exponential potential in a safe and co-regulated space.

Miller's description of cognitive limits is critical for information processing, knowledge retention, and learning with deep understanding. Hebb's

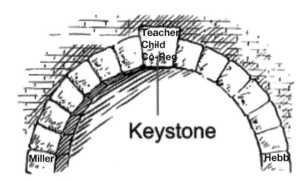

FIGURE 8.1 Keystone Architecture for Learning

addition to learning: neuronal firing as cognitive rehearsal is essential for growing/myelinating structures. The construct of cognitive rehearsal involves circuitry and myelination of white matter tracts through connecting all lobes with the learning moment. This is the genius of the teacher: the capacity to connect each individual child's brain with any content. Miller's Law is primary. Hebb's Rule is secondary. Teacher/student dyadic dance is tertiary. Together, this interaction supports robust pillars of pedagogy to engage children. The teacher-student co-regulation greenhouse forms the keystone that solidifies the architecture.

When in 2000, Professor Cowan (*68*) from the Department of Psychological Sciences at the University of Missouri, revised downwards the storage capacity of a child's working memory from 7 +/- 2 to 3–5 units, this critical information escaped under the radar for most teachers. Cowan links (as most teachers would) the child's "focus of attention" with the child's ability to "chunk" information and hold it in memory long enough to comprehend the whole.

> The fundamental capacity limit appears to coincide with conditions in which the chunks are held in the focus of attention at one time; so it is the focus of attention that appears to be capacity-limited (*68*).
>
> (p. 114)

It might even be the most important tool for teachers in classroom practice. In other words, teachers need to have a mental model about channel capacity, within which learners can retain and manipulate a handful of concepts in the conscious mind.

Teacher Talk

Partnering with Miller and Hebb in the classroom delivers change that fosters agentic learning and comprehension.

What was Surprising?
Teacher #1

I was surprised to discover that I spent 15 years in the classroom and never heard of Miller's Law. This is simply fascinating that there is a date for the Cognitive Revolution. Again, I had heard of a cognitive revolution, but I knew nothing about it.

Teacher #2

I was very surprised to learn that our telephone number is associated with Miller's Law. I never even considered it a "thing"—the number of digits in a telephone number.

What we already knew but now see in a new way?

Teacher #1

I am beginning to think that my iPhone is my working memory space—or at least an extension of it. I had a moment of disequilibrium last week, when I lost my phone and suddenly realized I didn't even know my daughter's phone number. When I got my phone back, I downloaded my contacts on paper so that I don't feel so dependent on the device anymore.

Teacher #2

I knew that the child's brain manages difficult new concepts by consuming much-needed short-term memory resources, but I hadn't considered my ability to increase those resources. This changes everything. From now on my job is to grow that tiny working memory space for my students. What a revelation!

When I consider a young child whose neural structures are not yet fully developed, I am dumbfounded. It takes time and practice for neural circuitry to connect the lobes and to strengthen with myelin.

If I put myself in the place of a typical child in my classroom, I can see how it might become a stressful, overwhelming, and deeply distressing space. Most of my children show up in a state of hyper-vigilance. I now realize that their amygdala hijacks their higher-order rational brain, interrupts normal processing in the prefrontal cortex, causing them to be easily overwhelmed, afraid, insecure, fearful, self-denigrating and a host of other negative beliefs. Then Reticular Activating System (RAS) picks up on this, and so, the downward spiral progresses.

What we need help with?

Teacher #1

How can I individualize my effort so that all children are growing their working memory at the same time? Do I have to do it one child at a time?

Teacher #2

Most of the issues that show up in my classroom do not begin in the classroom—they come from the playground, or the cafeteria, or the school bus. What can I do to help get this information to the bus driver, the lunchroom attendants, and the playground monitors?

Strategies for Change

Having spent years in the classroom without Miller, I can safely say that it is much easier with Miller. Add Hebb, and school life becomes amazingly easy and fun. Discipline entanglements go away, and children become the learning machines, which they are innately. I love the cognitive revolution. In retrospect, I think about how I could have missed it. But we all missed it. I was not alone in my struggle with children who did not react well to rewards and punishments. I raised children without Miller and Hebb. It makes a difference.

Simple Strategies

Put simply, Miller's Law (adjusted by Cowan) means that in the classroom, educators are mindful of the innate biological limitations that all children experience with their working memory. Invariably, some kids will be able to manage three or so new concepts, but most kids will be comfortable handling less than that. Neural educators learn very early that the most important practice to bring to every lesson is the ONE big idea. When the children leave this class, what is the ONE big idea that they take with them. The only way this can occur is if the teacher is intentional about that ONE big idea. If I know what the ONE big idea is, then the children will have a chance of picking up what that ONE big idea is.

Summary

In this chapter, we reviewed two pillars of pedagogy that are neurobiological. In the first case, George Miller defined the limitations of human working memory to be seven units plus or minus two. Subsequently, Nelson Cowan adjusted this number down to three or four units. For educators this is significant and helps explain cognitive overload, difficulty with attention, and points to reasons why some children act out and are disruptive in classrooms. Recommendations are offered to alleviate common discipline issues by adopting a neural position with regard to working memory, cognitive load, and attention.

Vocabulary

Miller's Law, Working Memory, Myelination

Notes

1. Miller presented his paper at the Special Interest Group on Information Theory held by the Massachusetts Institute of Technology. Cognitive Revolution = 91156, SIG, IT, MIT. Other papers that appeared at that notable meeting were prepared by scholars who pioneered work in Artificial Intelligence, linguistics, neuroscience, and Economics: Alan Newell, Noam Chomsky, Donald Hebb, and Herbert Simon.
2. Miller has been cited more than 32,000 times in academic articles as of this printing. Cowan recounts that George Miller was a humble man who never dreamed that his article would have become so important.
3. Ericsson was investigating questions of skill-based expertise and psychology at the Royal Swedish Academy of Engineering Sciences when Herbert Simon 'discovered' his research and invited him to Carnegie Melon to explore questions relating to expertise and cognition.

9

Hebb's Rule and Cognitive Rehearsal

I never questioned repetition until now.

—*Teacher*

Donald Hebb was a consummate teacher. Even in his early career at age 24, he experimented with methodology to eliminate drudgery and improve academic outcomes. Intuitively, he was convinced that the school experience that he was asked to deliver did not serve his students well. Having witnessed children of all intellectual abilities fail, he was convinced that the system was not in sync with how they best learned. In his own school days, he survived the vestiges of a pseudo-British "class" structure, which he considered mired in punitive practice that further damaged children's motivation to learn. In the 1920s, Montreal's education system reflected a neo-colonial mish-mash of "payment by results" and "monitorial" rote. Punishments were meted out liberally for behaviors that contravened the school's ethos. Assuring his students that education was a privilege, Hebb shifted from teaching by "lecture" to a co-created model by "flipping" the class. He did away with homework. In his own words, "Students were NOT punished for inattention and those who disrupted the class were sent outside to PLAY (78)."

After a brief interlude in formal classroom education, Hebb returned to scientific research on his favorite subject—the brain. He expanded his thinking in relation to pedagogy by deepening his connection to the biological basis of behavior. Being excited by neuro-physiological behavior, he sought to understand how the function of neurons contributed to psychological processes such as learning. Inspired by early successes, he devoted energy to enhancing the connection between pedagogical knowledge and neuroscience. Hebb was one of the earliest neuro-educators who believed that all behavior was the result of brain function (79).

Hebb Abandons Behaviorism

The educational world was struggling with an emergent behaviorist agenda that had sprung from the stimulus response laboratories of Pavlov, Thorndike, Watson, and BF Skinner. Skinner's radical behaviorism was prominent in Hebb's day, and called for a rejection of introspection by refuting mental and subjective experience. In Skinner's view, laws that were determined by a rigorous application of stimulus/response inquiry could explain all human behavior.

Hebb had already witnessed lesions in brain regions of psychiatric patients and was headed in a different trajectory. His educational experience in the classroom only served to solidify his medical experience in the surgical laboratory. The study of patients with brain injuries had convinced Hebb that it was the brain that explained behavior, and that teaching adolescent learners involved a journey into brain regions specific to consciousness, attention, perception, thinking, and emotion. Today, Hebb is recognized as a pioneer in the field of cognitive neuroscience. Gazzaniga, who established the field of split-brain research at the University of California, further describes him as the key individual who exposed behaviorism for its negative impact on education (29). Speaking about Hebb's 1949 publication *Organization of Behavior: A Neurophysiological Theory*, he states:

> Hebb took the psychological world by storm by boldly stepping into the black box of the brain thumbing his nose at the off-limits constraints imposed by the empiricist Hume and by behaviorists.

Not everyone understood how radical behaviorist thinking was changing the learning world. The neat unified theory that behaviorism offered wasn't passing muster with neuroscientists.

In a previous chapter, we pointed out that George Miller had rejected Skinner's external stimuli/response outcomes. He, too, was convinced that the primacy of innate mental capacities would win out. In the following account, Miller describes how he ended up (along with Hebb and Chomsky) in a counter-revolution, which we now recognize as the cognitive revolution. The jargon didn't work! (80)

> The behavioral revolution transformed experimental psychology in the US. Perception became discrimination, memory became learning, language became verbal behavior, intelligence became what intelligence tests *test*. By the time I went to graduate school at Harvard in the early 1940s the transformation was complete. I was educated to study behavior and I learned to translate my ideas into the new jargon of behaviorism. As I was most interested in speech and hearing, the translation sometimes became tricky. But one's reputation as a scientist could depend on how well the trick was played.
>
> (p. 141)

Scientists like Miller, Hebb, Simon, and Chomsky moved quickly beyond behaviorism, advancing their respective fields away from stimulus and response thinking.

Meanwhile, behaviorism embedded itself even deeper into education. In the following year, 1957, when Sputnik forced a reevaluation of American connection to math and science, the drive to win the race for dominance colored everything educational. Schools were key. Without considering any alternatives, behaviorist teaching methods became entrenched deeper into American education systems. The race was on. Some call it the race to the bottom. This might be the single great tragedy of schooling in the 20th century—to miss the cognitive revolution primarily at the conceptual level and, specifically, in practice.

A Biochemical Correlate

Hebbs' central thesis has implicit meaning for every teacher in every classroom. His notion that there is "a biochemical correlate for everything that people think, feel, remember, say, and do" is central to teacher preparation courses (78). From that standpoint, all conversations concerning a child's "bad behavior" are entirely out of place and, specifically, if they preempt progressive punitive practice.

In an amygdala hijack scenario, behavior is not "bad;" it is 'expected.' From Hebb's neural vantage point, all children want to excel in school, to be successful, and achieve success both academically and socially. But, if the conversation is about "bad behavior" instead of amygdala hijack; about punishment instead of strategies for increasing working memory; and about threats and consequences instead of brain derived neurotrophic factor, then the teaching profession is out of synch with Hebb's world of neural plasticity, long-term potentiation, and cognitive rehearsal.

Cognitive neuroscientists since Hebb's day have advanced the field by reaffirming his findings (81). With the use of advanced imaging techniques, they demonstrate the impact of impoverished environments on children's brains. Children who grow up in trauma, who suffer neglect, and who live in fear and hyper-vigilance develop smaller brains with less dendritic arborization (37). In the classroom, such a child will appear with "behavior" problems that look like disruption, aggression, and willful destruction. A neural educator knows how to use mirror neurons, neurotransmitters, and chunking to help any child co-regulate first and then grow structures that the brain requires for academic success.

Hebb's inspiration was grounded in children's play. In particular, he learned from his two daughters' play with pet rats that were running freely around their home. Given what he knew about running rats through mazes at his laboratory at McGill University, he pondered the question: "Are the rats who play with my daughters different from those isolated as caged animals at the office?" He realized that the brain was changing in response to environmental interaction—what we know today as epigenetics. Hebb's question set in motion a research trajectory that changed the lives of children and classrooms everywhere.

Teacher Talk

The art of teaching deteriorates quickly into cat and mouse games when rat play is taken out of the mix. Teachers who practice their profession without meaningful knowledge of Miller's Law or Hebb's Rule are consigned to behaviorist methods that rarely meet muster.

What was Surprising?
Teacher #1

I was surprised to learn about Donald Hebb. I can't believe that I have been teaching for so long and never heard of his important work for teachers.

Teacher #2

I was very surprised to learn that there is a biological correlate for everything we say and think. I had never thought about it like that.

What we already knew but now see in a new way?

Teacher #1

I knew that the brain is plastic, but now I see it in everything I do. When the kid has a good experience, the brain responds and grows structures that are supportive of that experience. And when the kid has a bad experience, the brain grows structures that support that bad experience. Makes sense!

Teacher #2

I knew that the brain was impacted by trauma and neglect. I am thinking of my students of color. They have endured a lifetime of unconscious bias and marginalization simply because of where they were born and the color of their skin. This connection to neuroscience and plasticity makes a lot more sense when I view my work with these amazing children. Racism impacts their brains every day. Many white people can't handle talking about racism. They get really uncomfortable; they clam up or say something like they are ok because they are "colorblind." They hide behind this term. I realize now how words are so important. I too have used words that center "whiteness," words that erase the harshness of discrimination and segregation. I can do better. I now see that many of the children who show up in my class are working with trauma. I am amazed to learn about dendritic arborization. That was a concept that I had not been aware of in the past. And to think that what I do—what I say—for that child can cause dendritic arborization to grow or shrink—that is powerful.

What we need help with?

Teacher #1

I am beginning to understand the workings of Action Potentials, but what is Long-term Potentiation? And if Dr. Hebb discovered it in 1947, how come I didn't learn about it until today?

Teacher #2

Where does ADHD fit in with all this talk of plasticity? Is ADHD something I can fix in my classroom, because I see a lot of kids who just can't keep still? They can't pay attention. They don't know how to focus.

Strategies for Change

Several strategies that are Hebbian in character are easy to introduce to the classroom or Zoom classes for social distancing spaces.

Simple Strategies

Replace the word "Repetition" with "Cognitive Rehearsal." Repetition is always meaningful for learning. We know that rote works. *One and One is Two, One and Two is Three*, and so on, helps us sing our "tables" so that over time we can recall the answer to complicated math in automaticity. When the brain is in automaticity, we free up working memory so that there is more room for other more immediate processing. Cognitive rehearsal trumps repetition every time.

When we think about Hebb's idea of neurons communicating with each other and that the presynaptic events on the first neuron can increase postsynaptic receptors on the connecting neuron, then we can be more intentional about how we engage the child's lobes with respect to a particular new concept. Figure 9.1 illustrates the cerebellum and four lobes. Cognitive Rehearsal will involve vision (occipital), listening and talking/arguing (temporal), movement and balance (cerebellum), small-motor skills and emotions (parietal), and the executive higher-order thinking and planning (prefrontal cortex). Cognitive Rehearsal initiated with intention can grow and strengthen structures that facilitate learning with deep understanding.

Advanced Strategies

Visualize each child in your class. Could you right now name three other people (assuming that you are one) who you consider are solid support people

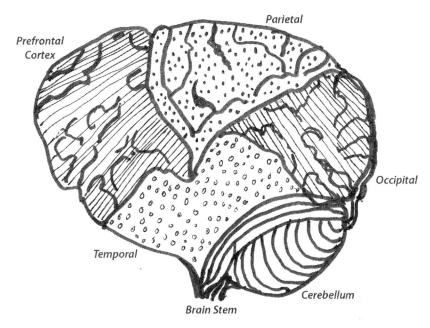

FIGURE 9.1 Cerebellum and Four Lobes

for that child? Each child requires four supporting adults to ensure safety, confirmation, reinforcement, and fun. Think outside the faculty room (you might have to think outside the home also). Yes, it might be that some kids will have four faculty that they know will support them; you might include a bus driver, a sporting coach, a cafeteria worker, a janitor. It matters less what they are; it matters more that the child has a trusting, supportive relationship with at least four caring adults.

Summary

In this chapter, Dr. Hebb walked into our classrooms. If for the first time, then the change will be expressly momentous. The notion of Cognitive Rehearsal replaced Repetition. If his ideas about "neurons that fire together wire together" has already been in your classroom, then perhaps you were able to increase your knowledge about plasticity: to imagine maladaptive impact as opposed to beneficial consequences. Each brain is only three pounds, and it is all the child has. It is enough. In the next chapter, we will explore further the world that Dr. Hebb set in motion; that of neural adaptation, cell assemblies, and structural and functional plasticity, by introducing Marion Diamond, the neuroscientist who measured Einstein's brain.

Vocabulary

Structural Plasticity, Cognitive Rehearsal, Dendritic Arborization

10

Plasticity Is a Two-Sided Neural Coin

I'm so glad my brain is plastic, too.

—*Teacher*

Rats! Maze smart and maze dull. Pet rats! This is an extraordinary story of how an intuitive thought about "pet" rats versus rats in a "cage" changed classrooms forever. Dr. Hebb's two daughters were allowed play with pet rats in their house. In his laboratory at McGill University, Dr. Hebb studied caged rats. The question he settled on was this, "Would pet rats run the maze better than caged rats?" This little experiment evolved into the study of "enriched environments" that caused schools to look like colorful, stimulating, and fun ADHD places, today.

Playing in a house with furniture, stairs, lots of rooms, and interesting new spaces, as well as enthusiastically, loving, and caring keepers was very different to existing alone in a drab cage. Rats in maze experiments typically run courses with probes sticking out of their brains. These probes allow researchers to "map" what the rat is "thinking" as he (typically males) makes decisions along the complicated route to the goal— usually a sweetened drink from a sipper. If the rat turns left, turns right, turns back, and so on, the researcher can determine via the probes if the hippocampus, or the dentate gyrus, or the amygdala, or the neocortex is "lighting up."

In a nutshell, compared to rats that were confined in drab, uninviting cages, he found that his daughters' pet rats "aced" the maze. Inspired by this result, a team of neuroscientists in Berkeley, California raised baby rats in two different environments—impoverished and enriched. The impoverished environment was Spartan, stark, devoid of any toys or companions. By contrast, the enriched environment had all sorts of toys, a running wheel, and lots of other rats with which to socialize. When they studied the rats' autopsied brains later, they found that the enriched rats had significantly more of the chemical Acetylcholinesterase. This chemical is an important element of neurotransmission and involves both pre- and post-synaptic receptors. Translating this into learning, the experiment showed that rats raised in uninspiring cages in a laboratory were worse at solving problems than rats raised in stimulating environments.

This was monumental for learning communities. These "enriched environment" experiments showed, for the first time, a link between the chemistry in an animal's brain and its ability to learn. The results intrigued Marion Diamond, an early-career neuroscientist whose focus was on studying the human brain and its higher cognitive functions. She would spend the rest of her research career studying the effects of environment on the development of the anatomy of the brain (82). Upon reading the results of the chemical Acetylcholinesterase enrichment experiment, she began her career with this question, "I wonder if the anatomy of these brains would also show a difference?" If rats were raised in impoverished versus enriched environments, could she detect differences in the physical anatomy of the brain? And if so, could that be translated to human brains? This would be clear evidence of "nurture at work, not nature."

Comparing brain tissue from the two types of rat environment—impoverished versus enriched—Diamond found variations. The cerebral cortex of enriched rats was 6% thicker than the cortex of impoverished rats. It was highly statistically significant: nine cases out of nine showed the difference. In addition, she discovered that in several cortical regions, neuronal dendrites were larger and much more highly branched. She also documented that there were more dendritic spines and more synapses. It was a very important finding in the anatomy and physiology world that in turn, had follow-on implications for the learning world.

> This was the first time anyone had ever seen a structural change in an animal's brain based on different kinds of early life experiences.
>
> (82)

This was plasticity in action. Neural plasticity is the "ability of the brain to be modulated by experience."(83) In Figure 10.1, the image on the right

FIGURE 10.1 Dendrites on Right Chronically Stressed

describes "shrinkage" of neuronal dendritic branching resulting from an impoverished (stressed) environment.

Plasticity changed everything. The idea that there were critical periods for neural development was revised. Yes, there were critical periods that are essential in the neuronal migration and development of certain elemental functions (e.g., visual cortex and primary language development), but it was now obvious that the brain could reconstruct itself through experience.

Young people are incredibly plastic. Plasticity occurs also in adults throughout life. Plasticity also had a downside—this meant that thick branching and rich arborization in dendrites could be undone. By moving a rat, even after a few weeks, from an enriched environment to an impoverished environment, the brain underwent a reverse process and the rat soon looked just like all the other rats that were raised in drab cages.

Neuronal reorganization through circuitry thus introduced a new and disturbing realization—since functional and structural modifications can take place in the brain, it falls to the nature of the perturbation of the environment to decide whether the alteration will be beneficial or maladaptive. Today, we have educational principles that focus on trauma, neglect, abuse, and other adverse childhood experiences because we know that they can negatively impact a child's developing brain. From this realization came the notion that social and emotional learning has a critical place in every classroom. Stepping deeper into the neural enigma, knowledge about genetic and epigenetic factors means that when we teach to the Orchid Child we enhance the learning environment for all children.

If you are like most educators who read about Marion Diamond's groundbreaking discovery in 1963, you are probably thinking, "Enriched environments are better than impoverished environments when it comes to brain development." And you would probably agree that the same applies for children in schools across the world. Our children deserve the best (enriched) environments, classrooms that are filled with stimulating, colorful, educational "toys" and trappings to make them engaging and fun.

That is exactly what happened. Teachers excitedly hung colorful educational posters, charts, stickers, mobiles, maps, and more. Classrooms were filled with science and math charts, engineering and technological gadgets. Classrooms took on an unmistakable aura of Reading, Writing, and STEM through very encouraging and supportive teachers. Beginning in the 1970s and 1980s right through the turn of the century, classrooms were busy places with color and stimulation. Expectations were high.

But something was wrong! Improvements in learning were not panning out as anticipated. Academic outcomes didn't shine. Kids were as disruptive as ever, maybe even more so. Classrooms became scary places and, today, teachers have to have very specific language installed in their contracts that protects them from the children. Safety for teachers! This was unheard of before 1963.

So, what happened? It seems that accompanying the shift to make classrooms more engaging and more enriched came the epidemic of inattention (84). Suddenly, teachers were complaining about children who were not able to focus, not able to pay attention. These children had ADD and ADHD—new words had to be coined to capture the gravity of these issues that changed the front lines of learning. What we failed to take into account was that lab cages are imminently boring for rats—like placing them in solitary confinement. Rats do not live in solitary!

Normal living conditions for typical rats in the wild would be the equivalent of enriched. The "simulated" enriched environment only added confusion. In other words, we might be better off interpreting the experiment in the opposite way: instead of showing that extra enrichment beyond normal experience increases brain development, the truth is that severe deprivation reduces brain growth in important cortical areas. Normal is sufficient. Over-stimulation causes inattention and the disruptive cascading effects of disengagement. Looks a lot like ADHD.

Young Lady, That Brain Doesn't Change!

Marion Diamond, still early in her career, took her findings to her colleagues at Berkeley. Naturally, they were excited with the discovery, stating the obvious. "This is unique. This will change scientific thought about the brain (82)." In 1964, they published the results in a now famous paper, "*Effect of Enriched Environments on the Histology of the Cerebral Cortex*" and, in Diamonds own words, the world changed. "I found myself at a session on the brain at the annual meeting of the American Association of Anatomists in Washington DC. . . . I was truly scared. There were hundreds of people in the room and this was the first scientific paper I had presented at a big conference. I explained the projects as calmly as I could, people applauded politely and then—I'll always remember this—a man stood up in the back of the room and said in a loud voice . . ."

'Young lady, that brain cannot change!'

Teacher Talk

Marion Diamond influenced thousands of teachers in her illustrious career as anatomist. Today, she still joins neural educators who carry mental models about plasticity to children—synaptic plasticity for Long-term Potentiation, and myelin plasticity for strengthening connections and speedy processing.

What was Surprising?
Teacher #1

I am surprised at knowing so little about the history of plasticity. I never heard of Hebb, Diamond, or rat mazes.

Teacher #2

I am very surprised to know that environment shapes the brain. That means that everything I do in my classroom is important for my students' brains.

What we already knew but now see in a new way?

Teacher #1

I knew about plasticity! At least I thought I did. But everything I knew was almost backwards. I had not thought about the implications for ADD and ADHD in my classroom when I added the dangling mobiles and the colorful charts. Of course, it's incredibly stimulating for kids. I would even say it's causing overstimulation.

Teacher #2

I knew that children were attracted to shiny things, attention seekers. I even called some kids attention seekers and punished them for being just that. But, now I can see that they are doing exactly what they are supposed to do with the stimulation that is in my space. I am blown away to put the pieces together. It's as much about pruning as it is about making connections. I knew that children were making more connections at this developmental stage (ages 10–11). We can pay better attention because we have already pruned . . . they are still building and with that extra billions of firings they have to be attention seekers. It's as if they are hardwired attention seekers who cannot pay attention! My room is a brain's nightmare; I have so much attention grabbers on display.

What we need help with?

Teacher #1

I need help with understanding the connection between attention and ADHD. Are you saying that my colorful educational classroom is over stimulating for my kids and that is causing them to be ADHD?

Teacher #2

How do we teach kids how to pay attention? Is how to focus the same as how to pay attention?

Strategies for Change

If I brought a neural toolbox into my classroom, what are three things I would change right now?

Simple Strategies

Classroom layout is critical. Are you going to have a teacher space up front or in the back? Where is the screen? Is it to the side, up front, or in the back? These considerations may or may not be in the teacher's control. But we have to think about the way they impact the child the minute they walk through the door. Can they see themselves in this classroom as they walk through the door? How? Why?

Advanced Strategies

Stimulation is a very important consideration for the classroom. There is nothing wrong with wanting to present a beautiful, busy, colorful, inspiring, stimulating, mobile, chart laden, mathematical space, geographical space, writing space, spelling space, history space, as well as daily chores, calendars, birthdays, children's work space, and, and, and . . . do you see where this is going?

Classrooms can be incredibly fun places and incredibly overwhelming places. The surge of synaptogenesis that a child experiences up to about puberty is two times the adult. After that, their neuronal activity declines through pruning until it stabilizes in adulthood. Consider the Orchid Child, who is alive with synaptogenesis. This child is sensitive to light, to color, to sound, to smell, to tone, to body language, to windows, to doors, to children, to desks, to silence, to whispering, to laughter, to hot, to cold, to, to, to . . . do you see where this is going?

Here is the outcome of a longitudinal study that focused on the Orchid Child. Begin with blank walls. Invite the children in decision-making. Co-create the space. Where should we place the calendar for daily events? Add daily do's. Add calendar and classroom routines. When it comes to decorating the rest of the walls, ask for help from the children. They will create a space that is not super stimulating—just stimulating enough for safety, agency, and fun. Ask the children to decide with you. This is the first foray into Intrinsic Motivation.

For instance, in this study, the children got into self-selected groups and made decisions about the classroom décor. Each group "owned" a corner of the room. There were all kinds of colorful charts and affirmations, and school-focused positive designer statements in a collection in the storeroom. Each group chose what they thought would be suitable for their corner. They borrowed ideas from other groups' selection, but they each put their stamp of identification on their classroom space. In the end, they were proud of what they created. As a class, they decided on some important questions: (i) How long would the décor stay this way? Would they change it every day, every week, every month? (ii) Could they swap corners with other groups if they were willing to change? (iii) Could we bring in posters from home, animals, and such?

The interesting finding from this study was that children owned their classroom. They had a secure sense of safety in their "corner." Inattention and its insidious consequences went away (85).

Summary

In this chapter, we were introduced to one of the most influential scientists in several interconnected fields. Marion Diamond was an anatomist who specialized in the study of how environmental experience shaped the brain. Her work redrew the map about how we understood the human brain before 1960. Many of her findings had implications for teacher/student relationship in the typical classroom—some that had beneficial outcomes, and some that had less than beneficial interpretations.

Vocabulary

Environmental Deprivation, Critical Periods, Inattention

11

Purposeful Long-Term Potentiation

How could we not have found out about LTP earlier . . .

—*Principal*

Long-term Potentiation is one of the most exciting discoveries to come out of the insightful research in the neuroscience programs at McGill University in Canada. Dr. Hebb pioneered animal studies, which highlighted how a brain can manage memories; how neurons communicate; what attention means for learning; and how cell assemblies and wiring affect learning. In particular, his work spilled over into and helped create new models and theories that have important implications for teachers in their classrooms. Today, we associate Hebbian theory with methodologies in cognitive neuroscience that make use of techniques like cognitive rehearsal, intentionality with neurotransmitters, myelination of pathways, and especially, with long-term potentiation.

But here is the conundrum. Since the middle of the 1940s, Dr. Hebb has played a meaningful role in bringing new findings related to neuronal communication, short- and long-term memory encoding, and other insights into learning to the attention of neuroscientists and educators. However, most of his work failed to get translated into practice, processes that change what we say and/or do in the classroom, and how we teach. While most teachers have heard of oxytocin, myelination, or long-term potentiation, they have not thought about these constructs as something they might use in their lesson plans to engage students or inspire learning. And they certainly do not wake each morning with the idea, "I am going to wire my students for long-term

potentiation today." Yet, as soon as teachers "discover" that oxytocin revital-
izes every classroom, that myelination helps every child persist with difficult
concepts, that long-term potentiation improves every child's ability to retain
information and learn with deep understanding, they are all in.

Long-term Potentiation

Long-term potentiation sounds a little like Action Potential. Thus, long-
term potentiation has something to do with firing and neurons. It comes
down to electro-chemical processes at the synapse. Recall that the synapse
is the currency for learning. Figure 11.1 illustrates pre- and post-synaptic
gateways and receptors at any synapse. A single neuron can have more
than 10,000 dendritic spines, each culminating in a synaptic contact where
the cell of one neuron communicates by receiving input from neighboring
neurons.

Spines are intimately involved in plasticity. When they receive synaptic
input, receptors can grow, change, die away, and be born again in response to
environmental stimuli. For instance, you learned Spanish in school and were
quite good at it. For 15 years after school, you had no reason to use Spanish. You lost your ability to think and speak easily in that language. Then,
you went on vacation to Barcelona, and lo and behold, within a few hours
your prowess with Spanish was back. It was easy to add new vocabulary and

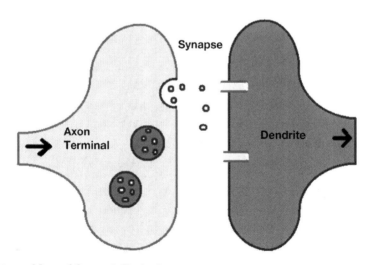

FIGURE 11.1 Normal Synaptic Excitation

carry on conversations with native speakers. Basically, when you received synaptic input from the Barcelona environment, receptors grew, changed, and were reborn in response to incoming stimuli.

This type of modulation is known as experience-dependent plasticity. Synaptic connections are processing sites that facilitate memory and learning, like that described in the Barcelona example earlier. Neuroscientists distinguish events from the environment that modulate synaptic activity by two features. They are mindful of (i) duration, and (ii) strength. Teachers get very fired up at the idea that it is possible to increase synaptic strength for their students, and that it could last for a long time.

Following on from Hebb's initial foray into cell assemblies and excitation processes, advances were made in the 1970s when a team of neuroscientists, Bliss and Lomo, expressly activated long-term potentiation in the synapses of anesthetized rabbits (86). Given that long-term potentiation occurs in the hippocampus—a location of the brain already known to be crucial for memory and learning—could teachers replicate this experience-dependent, long-lasting change for their students? Long-term potentiation causes spines to expand within seconds: the more the spines are stimulated, the bigger, more stable, and longer-lived they become.

Viewed together, Figures 11.1 and 11.2 describe the big idea behind long-term potentiation. The focus is on the synapse, the molecular space between two neurons. This is the juncture where neurons communicate. And neurons have to communicate so that your students can think, walk, talk, argue,

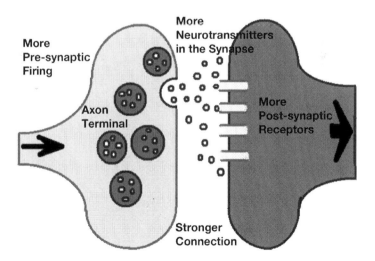

FIGURE 11.2 Increased Synaptic Excitation with Long-Term Potentiation

laugh, play, and so on. The first neuron (pre-synaptic) sends a message to the target neuron (post-synaptic).

The message is in the form of an electro-chemical transmission. First, the nucleus of the cell adds up the excitatory and inhibitory incoming perturbations. If a threshold is accomplished, the information is passed down the axon via an *Action Potential*. This involves an electrical charge that propagates down the axon as shown in Figure 11.3, towards the terminal. If the axon is myelinated, the action potential is faster and more efficient. Upon arriving at the terminal, the electric charge will engage with vesicles, causing

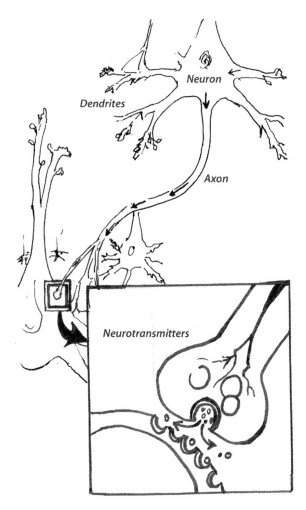

FIGURE 11.3 Action Potential Propagates Down the Axon

them to release chemical messengers (e.g., neurotransmitters like oxytocin) into the space between the two neurons—the synaptic cleft.

The vesicles that house chemical messengers are on the left side—the presynaptic terminal space. The synapse separates the dendrite of the target cell from the terminal of the firing cell. On the post-synaptic side, receptors are waiting to receive the chemical messenger. The number and size of these receptors is an important factor in the propagation of the action potential and chemical messenger from cell to cell. With a concentrated burst of neuronal excitation (a tetanus) on the pre-synaptic side, more receptors respond on the postsynaptic side. In turn, more neurotransmitters are expressed into the synaptic cleft, and the strength of the connection is increased. Figure 11.4 is

FIGURE 11.4 Long-term Potentiation Using White Board One-Word

an example of intentional cognitive rehearsal and focused potentiation using one-word summary and a good night's sleep.

The end result is important for learning and memory. While it is not a case of more is better, it is a matter of just the right amount—the Goldilocks Principle (87). Too much can be overload. Too little can be impoverishing, but just the right amount is perfect. Better connection means increased myelination; more neurotransmitters means a better chance to focus and stay engaged; and more excitatory action potentials means more post-synaptic receptors. In short, the student is active, attentive, and happy.

Teacher Talk

Long term Potentiation is not new to neuroscientists—they have been uttering excitement about the importance of this discovery for learning and comprehension since the middle of the last century. It is, however, new for teachers who are only now discovering important implications for learners when mental models align with how the brain works.

What was Surprising?
Teacher #1

I am surprised that I am only now learning about long-term potentiation—this makes me realize that every word I say, everything I do, and every thought I have needs to be intentional.

Teacher #2

I am so surprised to find out that I have so much immediate power over my own brain and, at the same time, over my students' brains.

What we already knew but now see in a new way?
Teacher #1

I knew that plasticity was a thing. I knew that children's brains could change. But I now see that I can cause these brains to really shine with intentional spiking in a few minutes. I am thinking that if the child feels safe, feels important, and welcome in the learning space, that they will generate ideas, myelinate ideas, and co-create the space. This is a new language for me.

Teacher #2

I knew that cognitive rehearsal was not the same as repetition! I get that. But now I see that cognitive rehearsal is a way to induce long-term potentiation. I hadn't thought of it before. I guess I was just switching "repetition" for "cognitive rehearsal" without really knowing the why or the how. The detail is important—subtle, but critical. I get the idea of repetition of non-declarative knowledge to reach automaticity for skills. For instance, improving my tennis swing by repeated trials, being mindful of the mediation from my coach. Over time, I myelinate a new pathway that causes my swing to be like the powerful swing he is teaching me. Then, thinking about learning and memory, I love the idea of increasing synaptic firing through cognitive rehearsal, tied to consolidation with REM sleep. I had not put that together before. I learned something new. I turn my focus and attention to it through cognitive rehearsal, using each lobe to visualize it, explain it, use highlighters to internalize it, and argue with my colleagues about it. I draw a picture to summarize what it means to me. Then I sleep and allow it to consolidate in REM. Next day, I go back to that picture and show it to a new person, explain what the concept means to me, and why I choose this particular picture to capture my thoughts. This is long-term potentiation in action. I love it.

What we need help with?
Teacher #1

Help me understand the idea that pre-synaptic excitation bursts can affect post-synaptic receptors so that my students are better prepared to learn. What do I have to do in my classroom to cause this to happen? Can it happen every day?

Teacher #2

How do we differentiate something like long-term potentiation when all brains are so different?

Strategies for Change

The individual brain is unique and in its uniqueness can accomplish truly amazing things. Yet, all brains describe similar systems, circuitry, and functions that are determined by genetic codes and environmental stimuli. Beginning at the bottom, wiring connects, integrates, and optimizes structures that allow children to survive, learn, and memorize new things, and contribute in many higher-order ways in a cognitive world. Long-term potentiation is a natural process. It can be augmented with learning systems, which are derived from mental models that are aware of, and understand how, structure enables function and plasticity enables conceptual change. What we teach in the classroom during the day is consolidated for the student in REM sleep at night.

Simple Strategies

Safety is first. When the child does not feel safe, the pre-synaptic firing will not occur with reference to the new content you are teaching. The child will be focused on survival. Questions that will fill the child's executive thinking will emanate from the hindbrain region that is associated with safety and fear. Questions could look like: "Am I in the right place; am I good enough; is it safe; what is coming next?" In addition, a child's self-talk might be negative: "No one likes me; I hate school; I am no good at math; teacher likes her, not me; my hair is a mess, my clothes are hand-me-down."

In a world where exclusivity and implicit bias predominate, it is critical that each teacher address their own biases with regard to their learning environment. Answer the following questions and think about (i) intentionality, (ii) agency, and (iii) metacognition.

- ◆ Can the child "find" herself in my classroom?
- ◆ Is there a picture or graphic that helps the child identify with my classroom?
- ◆ Is the child "seen" in my classroom?
- ◆ Is there truly a space for the child's voice?
- ◆ Am I being intentional about reaching every child?
- ◆ Am I using loaded words like "mom" and "dad" instead of guardian or caregiver?
- ◆ Am I still referring to my students as "guys" instead of "learners" or "scholars?"

- Am I referring to different abilities instead of disabilities?
- Instead of reading the children's names on the first day, do I ask the children how they would like to be addressed?
- Do I refer to students as "gifted" or "title-one" or "IEPs" or some other label that stratifies them?
- Do I use terms that include everyone?
- Do I single out a child for "reminders" or "behavior?"
- Do I call my class "boys and girls?"

Know better and do better. It starts with a mental model, then words, then cognitive rehearsal.

Vocabulary

Long-term potentiation, REM, Consolidation

12

Know Your Reticular Activating System

I knew that saying positive affirmations worked . . .

—Guardian

Behavior is infectious. Others will copy your behavior; you will copy someone else's behavior. And when you copy someone else, you change your brain. It's epigenetic: environment changes the brain. For that reason, environment is important. The brain can reorganize itself as a result of stimuli that are presented through external sources. In schools, we expect that mentors and leaders will present stimuli that are meaningful for each individual so that the brain adjusts in a good way. This is not necessarily always the case. Schools are establishments with as many hidden curricular constructs as those that are visible and tangible.

In every classroom, every playground, every cafeteria, every library, in fact, anywhere the child goes during a day in the life . . . there are socially constructed societal themes that affect the child's brain. How it plays out for any child depends on a number of factors that are complex, and as nuanced, as life itself. A couple of very definable aspect lenses, however, help explicate some outcomes.

Mental models matter. First, if we are aware of, and understand the construct "autonomic nervous system reactivity" for any student, then we can view social constructs through a neural lens that will help a student engage, and be successful, in school. Second, if we are aware of, and understand how labeling and stratification infuse an insidious counter-affect into any relationship-building process, we can avoid negative outcomes of classroom competitive practices. These two mental models will be made visible in relation to a critical survival structure at the back of each child's brain that can make the difference between success and failure in your classroom.

Reticular Activating System

The human brain is one of the most complicated and complex structures in the universe. Millions of bits of information need to be processed every second. The reticular activating system (RAS) acts as a filter that sifts through the incoming information—only about 1% is brought to conscious awareness. It is programmed (hardwired) to choose only the important information to bring to your attention. Millions of other bits are processed in the background that never arrive to conscious awareness—things like heart rate, blood pressure, temperature, and so on.

The decision to bring information to conscious awareness will be influenced by safety, survival, and beliefs. The reptilian brain is always concerned with survival, and is alert to anything incoming that could warn of danger. Additionally, voluntary bits that you, the user, deem important will be forwarded to consciousness. The RAS can, therefore, be a student's best ally when it looks out for safety. Conversely, it can be the worst enemy when it confirms the student's belief about her ability to learn. Imagine the following scenario:

> Sarah is a sensitive teen who does not function well with (i) competition, (ii) negative feedback, and (iii) high-stakes comparison with peers. It is time to get feedback regarding the three math problems they worked on earlier. Sarah is overcome with anxiety to discover the RED MARKS on her math test—pointing out calculations she did wrong. In fact, she is so overwhelmed with the sense of loss, fear, frustration, disillusionment, and distrust that she cannot attend to the gentle assistance that the teacher is trying to give her. Her own self-talk is deafening—defeating. Her breathing is short. Her voice, usually timid, has finally abandoned her—totally disappeared. She is afraid that tears will flow any moment. All she can hear are her own internal words, "I knew I was no good at math,"

"I'm the worst in class," "How can I ever hang around with Mary; she thinks I'm dumb."

The teacher was explaining that it's ok to make mistakes. "We learn from our mistakes." But, if you are no good at math—then you can't learn from mistakes. The self-talk won out. Sarah was despondent when she arrived home after school. She went straight to her room, shut the door, and cried herself to sleep.

RAS let her down. Actually, it did its work according to its function. As the filter in Sarah's brain, it looked for what was important to her. Whatever Sarah had decided to focus on, her RAS filtered incoming sensory information and delivered as she asked. Sarah already believed that she was no good at math. So, when her teacher corrected the part of the one problem that was incorrect with a RED pen, that was the filter that broke the camel's back. RAS controls focus and attention. Sarah didn't see the other questions, which were in fact correct. She didn't hear the part when the teacher told her that this simple error was a very small oversight and really didn't take from her understanding of the problem or the solution. All Sarah heard and saw were what her RAS allowed her to see and hear. It basically confirmed her beliefs. She was no good at math.

Your beliefs are important to your RAS—that is how it knows what you want it to focus on. When I say the words, "I can't bounce two balls; I am so uncoordinated." Then, that is what usually happens. Every time I drop a ball, the internal self-talk reminds me, "See, I told you . . . you can't bounce two balls." So why try! It's easier to just give up. Beliefs, self-talk, and proof follow each other around in a kind of self-fulfilling prophecy. RAS is constantly looking for things that you told it you believe. It doesn't matter to RAS if it's negative or positive. And the more proof you see (RAS confirms it for you), the stronger your belief is that it is true. "I'm no good at math, and teacher marks my paper with RED INK." In a strange self-fulfilling way, the stronger your belief is, the more likely you are going to tell yourself it.

Sarah's friend Chloe, on the other hand, is a resilient adolescent whose RAS is doing the same filtering process, but with a very different outcome. Chloe believes that she is pretty good at math. In fact, she doesn't really care either way. She basically does the bare minimum to get by in a class that is just ok for her. When she receives teacher feedback, she ignores the RED marks and approaches the mistake as just one of those errors that she missed because she was in a rush. When the teacher points out the detail that she had missed, she smiled. "Got this. We're good," and jotted a quick note on the page before consigning it to the folder where all the other "finished" work was hidden away forever. Chloe's RAS and Sarah's RAS are doing exactly the same thing—confirming their innermost beliefs.

RAS is part of our brain. And we can rewire our brain by building and strengthening new pathways. The more intentional and frequent we are about a desired change, the stronger the new pathway becomes. The RAS reacts to novel, and/or unexpected inputs, and through habituation blocks out familiar sounds that it "gets used to." For instance, the person who lives near the airport doesn't hear the airplanes taking off anymore, but the visitor to his house is shocked at how loud the noise is when they are directly in the flight path for departures. The RAS is activated. Similarly, in a crowded noisy room, a mom will detect her own child crying above the din.

Know your RAS. It is critical for survival, and you can make it your friend. It carries out crucial inspection by working ceaselessly in the background to keep the body functioning, even when we are at rest. The brain, as a whole, processes at something like 400 billion bits per second. It's a lot of checking and managing to make sure we are breathing and pumping blood. It controls information flow so that approximately 2,000 bits of information per second are allowed enter (*88*), and conscious activity works at about 60 bits per second (*89*). These filters protect the brain from becoming overloaded.

Teacher Talk

A small clump of neurons in the brain stem could play such a pivotal role in the classroom is critical information for teachers as well as students. Co-regulation that leads to self-regulation begins and ends with the Reticular Activating System.

What was Surprising?
Teacher #1

I am surprised that Sarah's RAS is the culprit. I see this everyday with some kids. It is a surprise that the solution is so simple. If I dispel with the RED PEN and focus on what she got right . . . build relationships around her successes. Then when she is confident enough to deal with the errors, we move on to the errors. It is so easy. I can't believe I didn't know this.

Teacher #2

I am so surprised to learn that my brain confirms my beliefs through a tiny clump of neurons that are more associated with attention, arousal, and sleep.

What we already knew but now see in a new way?
Teacher #1

I knew that Social Emotional Learning (SEL) was important, but I now understand that I hadn't differentiated between implementing for Affect versus Effect. I now see that we can't do both. I didn't notice that my rewards and punishments were driven by Effect. I was focusing on academic outcomes, basically abandoning relationship building with my students. Yet, we are a SEL school. I hadn't connected the dots. All the while realizing that the academic outcomes will improve when I make strong relationships and support the child's emotional needs. Relationship building is my new goal.

Teacher #2

I knew . . . somewhere in the back of my head . . . about the concept of "social constructs" . . . the idea that society creates meaning about facts and events (kind of in the background), and most people accept without questioning them. For instance, I knew that race and gender were social constructs. As we grew up, we "picked up" ideas about how race and gender fitted into society—from our guardians, from our teachers, from our coaches, from media, and from our peers. It's as if it was always that way. I, like everyone else, have implicit biases with regard to lots of things in the world. I rarely questioned my social constructs until I went to college. That was a while back. But, thanks to teaching with a neural kit, I am beginning to question social constructs that are in my day, in my school, and in my life. I try to "make visible" what my implicit biases are. I look for help from my community of neural educators. This RAS passage stopped me in my tracks. It exposed a social construct that is very alive in my mind that speaks to what is happening in my classroom. Teachers have reticular activating systems just like everybody.

Teachers have RASs Too

This was an eye-opener for me. The way I looked at children's behavior and how I described them . . . socially constructed. I can see now that I was totally binary. It was either "good behavior" or "bad behavior." Sometimes that looked like 'compliant' or 'non-compliant.' Terms that describe children in my school sound like this: "disrespectful," "defiant," "disruptive." We see compliant students as "normal" and non-compliant as "at risk" or "high risk," anything but normal. I spent most of my teaching time "managing" the bad behavior, non-compliant students, and disruptive, disrespectful, defiant kids. I know that **all** behavior is communication. It makes sense now that when I describe behaviors in binary terms I activate my RAS to think about kids as BAD or GOOD. Yet, we as teachers must create and deliver cognitive rehearsal around messages and understandings of behavior as complex and nuanced. Behavior is communication. Behavior indicates that students need increased relationships, increased structures, and/or increased skills. I am grateful to reignite my methods and practice with this refreshed perspective. I am changing my vocabulary. Out with the "Good," and "Bad" descriptors, and welcome words that describe what is really going on with the child—in the brain. Amygdala hijack, stress, anxiety, labeling, stratification, building structure before function, understanding the spiral effect of reticular activating system. This is a game-changer for me.

What we need help with?

Teacher #1

I need help to understand the difference between intrinsic bias and selective attention?

Teacher #2

How do we recognize the child who is so sensitive that she will not take kindly to criticism even when it is well intentioned?

Strategies for Change

Plasticity and Reticular Activating System can work to be the teacher's best friend or conversely worst enemy. Get to know the connection, be familiar with methods that grow structures, so that function is not leading the equation. Structure has to come first.

Simple Strategies

Relationship building is critical for "teach to the orchid." How the teacher uses her voice makes a difference to a hyper-vigilant student. She is expecting to be rejected, overlooked, punished, singled out, and made to feel stupid. Use voice to be welcoming, available, and supportive. When the classroom is fun and engaging, there is a higher potential for learning to occur.

Voice Can Be Used to Build Relationships

- Speak in a different cadence
- Adjust voice, tone, and inflection
- Intentional pauses increase novelty
- Suspenseful pausing builds anticipation
- Use gestures while talking

Movement Is All About Knowing How to Make a Safe Space for the Orchid Child

- Be intentional and thoughtful about how you interpret your space
- Stand still when you are making an important point. Repeat it, tell it again, and reinforce
- Move strategically across your space when you are asking a question to facilitate discussion

Storytelling Is an Important Attentional Focus for the Orchid Child

- Illustrate important concepts through storytelling
- Use visual aids and photographs, colorful cartoons, and charts
- Use cultural items from the children's world so that they can see themselves in your class
- Use humor; RAS loves an attentional jolt

Co-create Your Space With the Students

◆ Help Students represent their learning with mind maps, diagrams, and simple sketches
◆ Use scaffolding questions that allow students to find their voice in a metacognitive moment
◆ Use fun oxytocin brain breaks

Vocabulary

Reticular Activating System, Attentional Focus, Self-Talk

13

Mindset Matters

I try to be in a growth mindset, but I wonder . . .

—*Bus Driver*

Mind is to brain as walking is to legs—only a billion times more complex! The various functions of mind (thinking, feeling, acting, learning, remembering, and creating) are a set of processes carried out by the brain (*90*). The brain makes us who we are, producing every emotion and intellectual act. The brain therefore, determines our moods, endowing us with the capability for great joy, and when circumstances change allowing us to experience terrible misery. Mind is a person's intellect—a facility that enables awareness of our world, including possessions and obsessions we experience in it. Mind, as the faculty of consciousness and thought, enables us to think and to feel.

A mindset is a particular state—a "frame" of mind. While one might have a particular frame of mind about a person, place, or thing, it can be changed. This is the critical difference between mind and mindset. The functions of mind are carried out by brain. If a person decides to change the frame of mind, brain will carry out that function. We distinguish two states for mindset—fixed and growth. Growth sounds and feels better. But most people do not understand the nuance associated with mindset—either fixed or growth. In thousands of tests, empirical evidence indicates that the majority of people are convinced that (i) they only use 10% of their brains, and (ii) they are stuck with the brain they were born with (*91*).

FIGURE 13.1 Misinformed Mindsets

As shown in Figure 13.1, candidates in courses that focus on the connection between neuroscience and learning can choose to place a sticky note on one of these four choices:

1. We use 100% of our brains
2. We use 10% of our brains
3. We use 37.5 % (female), 25.5% (male)
4. We use according to the Pareto 80/20 Principle

It is always a surprise for participants to discover (i) the wide spread in data, (ii) the lack of knowledge about brain, and (iii) the correct answer. Most people will swear that they heard the 10% use theory from their teacher/professor or from their guardians. In like manner, they are convinced that they have a growth mindset, but couldn't explain in detail, what that entails.

Growth mindset sounds good. Feels good. But what does it mean? Why is one person's mindset "growth" and another's "fixed?" What constitutes the difference? Is my mindset always growth, or am I sometimes fixed? It's hard to find someone who proclaims, "I want to have a fixed mindset?"

Mindset can be confusing and frustrating for people even when they say they know exactly what it is and how it works.

Teacher Mindset

In this chapter, we will look at mindset from a number of perspectives. Carol Dweck's work on defining the impact of fixed versus growth mindset has shaped how teachers (and a lot of HR managers) look at how people show up in the classroom (or workplace). Other considerations come into play when it comes to neural substrates for mindset and how children learn.

It turns out that mindset and the Reticular Activating System are intimately con-joined. Recall that in the last chapter we learned how RAS confirms one's beliefs. Beliefs are at the heart of mindset. In addition, we look at the impact of mindset on the sensitive Orchid Child and compare that with how mindset affects a resilient Dandelion Child. The implications are extraordinary and reveal why many children fail to engage in learning spaces that they deem "unsafe." In short, mindset, reticular systems, and autonomic nervous system reactivity work together to define a child's standing in school and beyond.

The reticular system is located in the hindbrain—the reptilian, survival brain. It can be associated with a reactive response to incoming sensory data. Mindset is situated in systems that connect with reticular systems, limbic systems, and the neocortex. Rational thinking, emotion, and especially beliefs are thus crucial to mindset. The propensity to be reactive is always present in mindset—in particular, an uninformed mindset. For instance, if a child is unaware that people construct mindsets in making sense of the world, they are equally unaware that they can "adjust" their mindset. Mindset is easy to influence, and it can go negative just as easy as positive. The Reticular Activating System has a field day with negative mindset. In the following scenario, we meet Rachaela, a bright pre-teen who is vulnerable, impressionable, and hyper-vigilant (52).

Rachaela's Mindset RAS

> **Teacher:** [to class] Each of us, you and I, have brains with amazing capacity. Our brains have limitless potential. That is a lot of potential. As a result, we can learn anything, and become good at anything we put our minds to. That includes running, jumping, reading, writing,

science, math, and more. We just know that even if we can't play great soccer today, we will be able to with practice and coaching. Our brains are amazing.

Rachaela: (Crying . . . sobbing)

Teacher: There's the buzzer. Everyone, it's recess time. Have fun in the playground. Rachaela, I see you are upset; can I come and talk with you.

R: uh huh . . . ok.

T: I see you are sad? Can I help? Did something happen?

R: Uh huh . . . I was thinking about what you said . . . ummm . . . about my brain and my mindset. You said we can do anything. Even science and math and riding a bike.

T: Uh Huh. Yes. Even riding a bike.

R: Does that mean that my dad was wrong when he said that I am stupid and dumb and not able to do anything?

T: Oh, dear Rachaela, yes. Your dad is wrong about that. You have a great brain. You can do anything you set your mind to. In fact, in my class you are one of the smartest students. I see how you focus and pay attention and try your best. I am very proud of how much effort you put into your work.

R: Is my brain as good as the other kids?

T: Oh yes. Your brain has 83 billion (with a B for billion) neurons and each neuron has 10,000 connections. That translates into trillions (that's a huge number) and trillions of connections. Same as every other student in this school! Your brain is as good as any other child. And you, because you are a smart young lady, can ignore any negative chatter from your family. In this class, you are a trillion, trillion brain. Now have fun at recess.

R: (Smiling) I will. Thank you Mrs. O.

In Rachaela's world, binary predominates. Things are good or bad, right or wrong, smart or dumb. She was lucky to have a teacher who understands this peculiar binary world, who knows that there is a different "cognitive" world. Above all, she is fortunate to have a teacher who is capable of making visible and translating that binary world for someone who is trapped in a mindset that limits. Plasticity is to the cognitive world as fixedness is to the binary world.

Once we learn about just how malleable the brain is, and how powerful our beliefs are, we can no longer inhabit just the binary world. We are liberated immediately and forever into a learning space that is aligned with brain.

Rachaela was quick to change her mindset. She was ready and needed the support of a caring adult to help her walk through the "stretch "

The brain is always "listening". It listens for information that is critical for survival, telltale facts for determining a safe space, and, in particular, a safe "social context". The sensitive Orchid Child is also always listening, because she lives in a place of hyper-vigilance. For the sensitive child, social context can be anywhere: school or home, playground or school bus, hallway or cafeteria. Each social context has capacity for imminent danger, for anxious premonitions, and for reminders that they are often out of their depth, like limping baby zebras on African grassland. Social context defines her.

Let's give the dad the benefit of the doubt. Let's say he loves his daughter. Let's say he wants to toughen her up a bit and make her more resilient, because life is hard. Perhaps he thinks he is doing her a favor. Perhaps, he never said those awful words, but Rachaela picked up the meaning from his body language and, perhaps, from his tone when she overheard him yelling "support" at her softball game. She picked up on his disapproval about her strikeout when he didn't think she was listening. Orchid children hear everything, see everything, interpret everything as meaningful from a survival, trauma standpoint. They can internalize incipient trauma in an inner cauldron of chaotic fever. One thing is clear. Beyond dad's intention—whatever it was—the damage to Rachaela was immediate and forever.

RAS-iness Is All

Dweck's definition of mindset (15) goes to the heart of reticular RAS-iness. Her findings highlight two important constructs that pertain to learning—Intelligence and Talent. One's understanding of these constructs dramatically influences any academic outcomes and purpose. Children entertain mindsets that are instituted through interaction with family and school.

A child has a "self-theory" about herself with respect to intelligence and talent. This all-telling "self-theory" established itself with the aid of covert curriculums at school and at home, in an unconscious social assembly. The way the student defines herself with respect to intelligence and talent can have serious implications for present success in school, as well as future success in life. The bottom line is clear. When the student believes that intelligence is malleable—it can be changed—then her perspective on learning new things enhances her ability to be academically successful. She can easily understand that effort is the pathway to mastery; she is able to persist even when school is challenging.

Similarly, when she realizes that talent is not inherited, but the result of focused effort, she is willing to put in that effort, not give up in response to setbacks. In short, if she knows that getting smarter is simply a function of neural plasticity, she can transform her learning life with amazing knock-on upside for the rest of her life.

Mindset implicates a child's mental state with success or failure in school. Academic mindset refers to beliefs, but couples them with attitudes and ways of perceiving oneself in relation to learning and intellectual work. Mindset is therefore associated with motivation and students' readiness to engage in learning tasks. From this perspective, readiness is RAS-iness.

Teacher Talk

Mental models about talent and intelligence make all the difference when it comes to RAS-iness of learning. Self-talk that embodies informed neural thinking helps a child to find potential with academic outcomes that match.

What was Surprising?
Teacher #1

I am surprised that Rachaela's dad was so insensitive—so cruel.

Teacher #2

I am surprised to learn that mindset is associated with intelligence and talent.

What we already knew but now see in a new way?
Teacher #1

I knew that intelligence was measured. I know my IQ score. But I now see that my IQ can change. Intelligence is not a fixed quantity. In fact, by just reading this chapter, I probably increased my IQ score.

Teacher #2

I knew that some kids had talent, and some didn't seem to have any talent. But, I now see that the kids with talent really worked hard and expended great effort, usually with their guardians and coaches to get that talent. I now see that it was not something they were born with. I also see that all kids can have great talent, if given the opportunity. It really does have to do with plasticity.

What we need help with?
Teacher #1

I need help to understand the difference between fixed and growth? Do all orchids have a fixed mindset?

Strategies for Change

When we teach to the orchid, we are immediately engaged in a fixed mindset journey. Plasticity and self-talk become pillars of support for a child. Mental models that highlight these four points help liberate the child from a mindset that is fatalistic to a creative space:

1. How malleable the brain is
2. How effort is connected to talent and intelligence
3. How white matter structures can be built with simple concrete steps
4. How these same structures can be strengthened with cognitive rehearsal

Simple Strategies

Many teachers have embraced the notion of teaching to the orchid by helping them gain an understanding of fixed and growth mindsets. By graphically incorporated mindsets into zones of social and emotional regulation, they scaffold the child's ability to place themselves on a continuum. Mindsets play out differently depending on the child's autonomic nervous system reactivity. For instance, the Orchid Child typically displays a desire to look smart; the Dandelion Child typically displays a desire to learn.

By using a visual scaffold, the teacher facilitates a shift from fixed to growth along five constructs as follows:

- Challenges: Avoid or Embrace
- Obstacles: Give up Easily or Persist in the Face of Setbacks
- Effort: Effort is Fruitless or Effort is a Pathway to Mastery
- Criticism: Ignore Useful Negative Feedback or Learn From Criticism
- Success of Others: Threatened by or Inspired by
- World View: Deterministic or Free Will
- Life Outcome: Plateau Early or Reach Ever-higher Levels of Achievement

The RED Zone equates with FIXED Mindset; the Green Zone equates with GROWTH Mindset.

The chart explains the difference between "fixed" and "growth" by portraying a mental journey along a continuum. Figure 13.2 is a simple tactile scaffold that facilitates the child visualizing a difficult mentalistic construct

FIGURE 13.2 Visual Scaffold Helps Children Shift from Fixed to Growth Mindset

like mindset. At the same time, the visual scaffold that the teacher/child co-creates engages through (i) intrinsic motivation, (ii) a tactile model that represents the mindset journey, and (iii) peer-to-peer teaching when the child shows other children how to make the model and how to apply it to mindset.

Vocabulary

Deterministic, Intelligence, Mindset

14

Comfort Zone for Adaptive Expertise

Adaptive expertise connects so easily with 21st century skills

—School Counselor

The capacity to acquire expertise is one of the great and peculiar strengths of the human species (92). Teachers who have attained degrees and teaching credentials are "experts" in the art of pedagogy. Children who attend classes are also on their way to becoming experts at something. We are all experts in something. The question is, what kind of expert? This concept of expertise is not as simple as it first appears. In this chapter, we will explore what it means to be an "adaptive" expert as opposed to a "routine" expert, and how that might play out in your classroom. This particular nuance with regard to expertise is aligned with how the human brain works and, especially, with how children learn. Adaptive experts connect directly with the reptilian brain's Reticular Activating System in efforts to move beyond a fixed mindset. It concerns itself also with limbic (emotional) brain regions by co-regulating the child's fear-processing center (amygdala) through a metacognitive moment involving the neocortex.

A growth mindset is emblematic of 21st century skills that are important aspirations for successful educational outcomes. Typically described as the Four Cs (Critical Thinking, Creativity, Collaboration, and Communication), these skills are most sought-after as appropriate for students who graduate school and enter the workplace. Students are required to be more than just "prepared," but also demonstrate capacity for high performance.

Twenty-first century skills are necessary in order to align with today's world challenges: pace, stress, competitiveness, technological savvy, culture, and geography. We are living in a world that is reinventing itself every few months. Expertise is as important for students as it is for teachers in this fast-paced, competitive marketplace. The shift from routine to adaptive is a metacognitive moment that requires an experiential commitment. Teachers who embrace a paradigm shift from routine to adaptive expertise acquire a powerful framework with which to address 21st century skills. If a teacher cannot fathom adaptive expertise, then what chance is there for students to embrace a skillset that is critical, not only for survival, but also to thrive?

The Four Cs are essential in the drastically "changed" learning environment today, more than ever. Unintentional and unwelcome as it was, the recent COVID-19 pandemic outbreak demanded immediate survival strategies for a fractured educational roadmap. The ensuing solutions translated into profound and long-lasting repercussions for classroom learning and educational processes. This fifth C (Corona) did not constitute a curricular pillar in its own right, but rather imbued itself systemically across all aspects of school. Modern learning was asked to pivot from face-to-face to various combinations of blended, and/or distance methods.

We are in an information age. As a result of an overriding need to keep up, and an equally expedient need to manage technologically challenging delivery mechanisms, we realize a nuanced understanding of what it means to be an expert. In the past, theorists described a linear approach (93) that, for reasons largely tempered by political expediency, were grounded in these two Es: Economy and Efficiency. In the early 1900s, there was a desire to manage change with both economy and efficiency in mind. Taylor's *Time and Motion* studies (94) were adapted to solve the school question. Being a fledgling system in a new country and, given the economic needs of the time, efficiency won out.

Taylor's industrial model connected tightly with a third E—Thorndike's shift from **Affect** to **Effect**—and the pattern for high-stakes testing was set in motion. Figure 14.1 is a quick reflection about efficiency and economy when it comes to testing millions of children in a system that is anything but efficient or, for that matter, economic.

The typical school experience viewed the child as a factory product that, not unlike Ford's Model T transmissions on a conveyor belt, was en route to passing the test of approval and, thereby, becoming educated. This

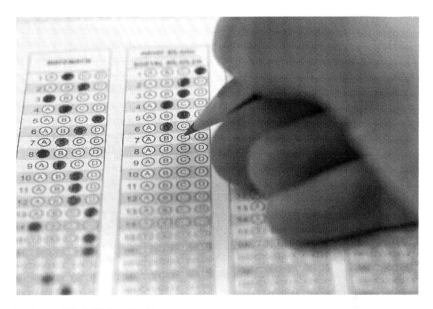

FIGURE 14.1 High-Stakes Testing

factory "conveyor belt" mindset was committed to "fixedness" detailed in routine thinking. This kind of thinking featured in Ford's audacious schema, which caused millions of cars of any color to be churned out "as long as they were black (95)." Ford's influence is also apparent in the following vision of education, as stated by E. P. Cubberley (1916), one of the founding framers of American public schools. His educational treatise "*Statement of the Fundamental Principles underlying the Organization and Administration of Public Education (96)*" detailed a burgeoning system, flexing under the strain of millions of new students who would attend school for the first time.[1]

> Our schools are, in a sense, factories in which the raw products (children) are to be shaped and fashioned into products to meet the various demands of life.
>
> (1916, p. 338)

The child was therefore a "novice" who progressed over time with practice to "expert." Figure 14.2 describes the typical linear progression on one domain—the X-axis. The child begins as Novice and progresses through a

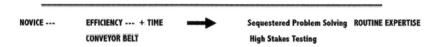

FIGURE 14.2 Transmission Model

standardized grading system towards a stamp of expertise. This signals the ability to move up to the next grade. Experience is the currency of a model that invests in practice over time. Children are grouped into classes, each class advances grade by grade, and measures of success are ascribed with Sequestered Problem Solving (SPS) high-stakes testing (97). Thus, the strange tug-of-war between thrift and efficiency was infused into the American educational system from the outset. At times, this transmission model was efficient (98), and at times it was cheap (99), but it never achieved the lofty goals that it targeted (51).

The concept of "adaptive expertise" involves a second dimension: processes that lead to innovation, and processes that lead to efficiency through well-practiced routines. These two dimensions are illustrated in Figure 14.3, an X-axis and a Y-axis. The horizontal dimension emphasizes Efficiency, the vertical dimension emphasizes Innovation. Mindset is the critical differentiator between the expert and the adaptive expert. A fixed mindset will preclude reflective measures that embrace and enhance flexibility and adaptation (100).

Most teachers agree that a Preparation for Future Learning (PFL) is exactly what education is about: to address chaotic, fast-paced social contexts that we find ourselves in today. Figure 14.4 highlights a non-linear curved path that draws from efficiency and creativity. This personalized pathway escapes a monotonic SPS world of "cheap" efficiency, and raises the bar to encompass neural, social, and emotional criteria that engages and inspires.

Teacher Talk

Paradigm shifts area easy in the rear-view mirror. When someone shows us the solution, we are shocked that it was so hidden prior to that moment. However, when one has experienced the paradigm shift, the elements of choice, decision, and definition bring closure and capacity.

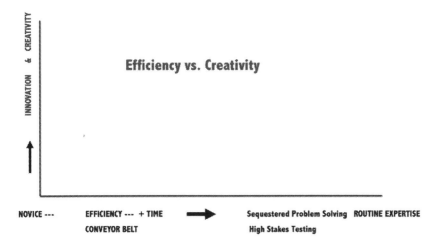

FIGURE 14.3 Two-Dimensional Model for Adaptive Expertise

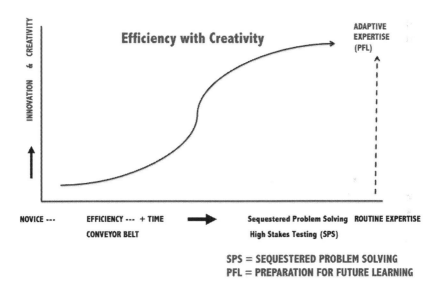

FIGURE 14.4 Adaptive Expertise Derives Preparation for Future Learning

What was Surprising?

Teacher #1

I am surprised to see yet another paradigm shift—routine to adaptive.

Teacher #2

I am surprised to learn about the 19th century factory model of learning and how pervasive it is in our system still.

What we already knew but now see in a new way?
Teacher #1

I knew that expertise was about 10,000 hours of practice, but now I understand that it's not so much the 10,000 hours, but the cognitive rehearsal and the intentionality.

What we need help with?
Teacher #1

I need help to visualize how to operationalize a shift from routine to adaptive, and encompass neural and mindset at the same time?

The following progression of Figures 14.5 through Figure 14.9 details the shift that is required of individuals when they adopt a growth mindset, decide to step outside their comfort zone, take a risk with threat response, and embrace the natural plasticity of a cognitive learning space.

In stage one, the novice typically finds herself in a safety bubble inside the comfort zone. The system tends to militate against stepping outside; thereby, rocking the proverbial boat.

In the second stage—the React Zone—any perturbation to the status quo will tend to prompt a reactive response. This phase is exemplified with ide-

FIGURE 14.5 The Comfort Zone

FIGURE 14.6 The React Zone

FIGURE 14.7 The Metacognitive Zone

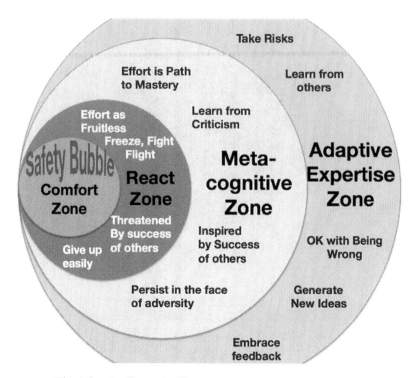

FIGURE 14.8 The Adaptive Expertise Zone

ations that look like; freeze, fight, flight reactive stance where effort is fruitless and being easily threatened by the success of others the novice will give up easily.

With careful mediation and co-regulation, it is possible to foster a moment when metacognition will engender a new pathway. This is the Metacognitive Zone. With this new vision, effort can be the path to mastery, the student can learn from criticism; they can become inspired by the success of others and might even persist in the face of adversity.

In the Adaptive Expertise Zone, the learner will be prone to take risks, learn from others, and will be ok with being wrong. They will generate new ideas and embrace feedback. The process of arriving at this growth space involved moving through the react space with the help of a metacognitive moment.

We outline the shift in thinking—the edge of expertise—as the moment when a co-regulatory process, enhanced through a metacognitive moment, resulted in an open and willing mentalistic stance that embraced the unknown. In this way, Adaptive Expertise fosters a PFL.

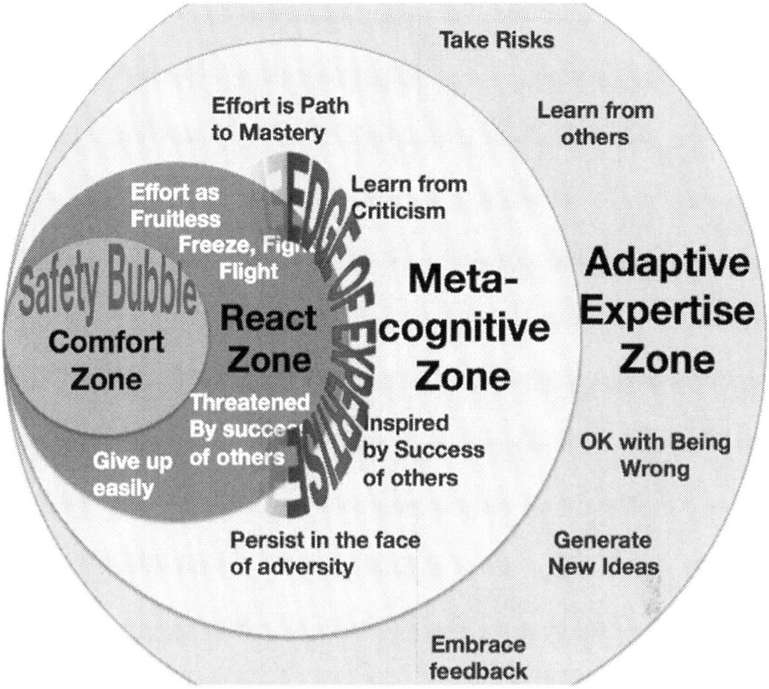

FIGURE 14.9 The Edge of Expertise

Strategies for Change

"What would I change if I used a neural lens?" This question is at the heart of the conceptual shift from a routine fixed place to an adaptive, growth space. Viewing the world from a growth mindset perspective means that you are aware of certain inalienable cognitive truths.

We believe that the following principles are real:

◆ Brain is plastic
◆ Intelligence is not fixed
◆ Children have immense potential

We believe that the following principles make a difference:

◆ Talent is grown through cognitive rehearsal
◆ Structures can be built
◆ Circuits can be strengthened through myelination

We believe that adaptive expertise is attainable:

◆ I step outside my comfort zone
◆ I overcome amygdala hijack
◆ I am metacognitive

Finally, adaptive expertise means replacing the old 3Rs (Reading, wRiting, and aRithmetic) with a cognitive 3Rs (Reflect, Revised Thinking, and Report Out).

Simple Strategies

In theory, it sounds just fine to state that, "I am creating a 'belonging' classroom in my school." But in reality, that takes a lot of work. Begin with intentionality. Many teachers think like this.

> I don't have enough time in my day to give every child enough time to really get to know them. When I am faced with the reality of devoting 20 minutes to chatting, listening, exploring what makes these children tick, then I am taking away from time that I would normally devote to math or science or English Language learning, and so on. Is it worth my while sacrificing 20 minutes of math time so that I can listen to little Juan tell me how he can do a belly flop in his friend's pool and everyone laughed?

It is a very common problem—too much content and not enough time. Deep down, teachers know better. Listening to Juan is probably the most important thing we do all day for him. And for Mary and for Jerome! Because our children get to know that we are interested in them. We are intentionally creating a purposeful community that is safe, fun, and about them.

The science is clear. Neural experts tell us that when we feel that we don't belong, our brains are in a hyper-vigilant state, persistently monitoring for threats. This leaves less cognitive resources for higher-order thinking and problem solving. Fear for safety, and a sense of isolation, take over. The end result is that the child is not set up for success in learning. We must be intentional about spending the time to get to know the children—so that they have a sense of belonging, a sense of community with safety, and fun. Then they can be challenged and stretched cognitively. This is where they find their voice to tell their stories. This is where they learn best.

Vocabulary

Adaptive Expertise, Preparation for Future Learning, Sequestered Problem Solving

Note

1. In 1890, only 4% of US youth graduated from high school. By 1940, half of US youth did.

Part III
Conceptual Collisions

15

Intrinsic Motivation in a Gift Box

Do you call this work? Does a boy get a chance to whitewash a fence every day?
—Mark Twain (Tom Sawyer, 1876)

Tom Sawyer was a motivation genius. Masterfully reframing a chore that his aunt obliged him to complete, he was able to engineer the situation in his favor, so that his pals felt compelled to pitch in. He may have been unaware of the difference between extrinsic and intrinsic motivation, but his creator, Mark Twain, endowed him with the intuitive instinct to understand how to manipulate his classmates into contributing *their* time and effort to *his* assignment. The icing on the cake was that they were willing to part with some of their treasured possessions for the privilege of taking part in the obligation.

In the fence-painting scenario, young Sawyer unwittingly fulfilled the three consequential principles inherent in intrinsic motivation: autonomy, mastery, and purpose. Nobody forced the children to join in the painting frenzy. Clearly, their sense of autonomy in making the choice to contribute was an important entry point. There is no better way to experience immediate mastery than in dipping a brush into white paint and watching it spread onto an old fence. It not only looks good, but it feels good. Results are tangible and clearly visible to everybody. Finally, sense of purpose is implicitly tied to covering the fence with white paint. The children had a clear purpose, made their own choices, and received immediate feedback that was consequential.

Motivation is key to learning. Interest is key to motivation. From the Orchid Child point of view, it's even more personal. Is it safe? Am I safe?

If I try, will I look stupid and fail? Interest is situated in the survival construct: "Me Here Now." If it is about me, where I am this minute, then I will engage. If it's about you, or something remote over there in some other time . . . I can't. My brain will introduce alternative scenarios that will prevent me from engaging. Thorndike was right! Interest revolves around feelings. If I do something and it feels good, I'll do more of it. If it feels bad . . . I'm out.

How can teachers motivate children to learn—especially the children who need it most. These are the children who are already a long way behind by the time they get to kindergarten. The learning lag only increases year over year, so that a student who arrives at middle school is more prone to act up, opt out, be disruptive, and eventually drop out.

A neural viewpoint views "lagging gaps" as missing or inadequate structures. So, we focus on growing the structures and then installing the function—math, ELL, science, and so on. Neural educators recognize that all students use kinesthetic, visual, and auditory pathways to take in new information, and that some students use different processing strategies at different times, depending on the context of the learning. In this next section, we apply a neural lens on structures.

Neural Lens on Structures

Children are born with the potential to be consummate learners. As a species we are hard-wired to learn. When neuroscientists look at brain scans of newborns they typically look very similar. Roughly 86 billion neurons make up grey matter material that is essential for the child's capacity to suckle, bond, reach out, coo, smile, cry, crawl, and. eventually, walk and talk. From birth to age three, huge change is observed. During this timeframe, infants gain more than a million neural connections every second.

One year later, when neuroscientists again look at the FMRI pictures of the same infants, the picture is very changed. Images will show different concentrations of circuits, different arborization patterns for dendrites, variation in number of synapses, and even differences in the physical size of critical structures including the cerebral cortex. Clearly, these changes are effects derived from environmental factors.

It is the job of neurons to communicate. They talk with one another in order to pass on critical information that allows the child engage with the world. In doing so, neuronal firing will form circuits. This circuit formation involves synapses, and occurs in bursts of "synaptogenesis" where social, emotional, and physical interaction with guardians and caregivers establish and amplify the infant's wiring. It takes a lot of years to arrive at maturation—usually around 25. Thus, children's brains are formed and grow to maturity in reflection of what goes on in the family and home.

Children arrive into kindergarten classrooms with very different abilities to learn. If all children were "ready" to learn, it would be easy to teach them, and results would be spectacular. But this is far from reality. Most children are not in this space. Recent studies indicate that two-thirds of children enter kindergarten unprepared for the demands that school places on them (101). General education (Gen Ed) classrooms are where these "demands" take place—they look like a one-size to fit all kids. Teachers quickly discover that a lot of kids can't fit.

Children, who struggle in Gen Ed classrooms, often are constrained by lack of hand-eye coordination skills that are required for simple tasks. They haven't yet acquired the functional capacity to tie their shoelaces, button their coats, or walk without crashing into other kids or just random furniture. From a learning point of view, these children do not have (i) requisite fine-motor skills to be successful in even the most meager of academic demands that require pencil and paper, or (ii) cognitive skills to know what to do with the pencil and paper for problem solving.

Consequently, some children are "pulled out" of Gen Ed classes and placed into Special Ed classes that seek to increase abilities deemed necessary to catch up. Typically, it's not a very successful proposition, because it requires a lot more time and effort than the typical IEP intervention can supply. Teachers usually have large caseloads, and children continue to struggle significantly. Sadly, these early lagging Gen Ed "pulled out" kids tend to be the same children that are later "pushed out" of General Education schools, to end up in either "alternative" schools or "juvenile detention"centers to complete their education (10, 45).

Front-line teachers, like occupational therapists (OT), will verify that 30 minutes a week for "specialty" skill building is not nearly enough time. In particular, that short amount of time is not sufficient to see any reduction in opportunity gaps. From a cognitive neuroscience point of view, establishing new circuitry and strengthening the connections requires not only time, but also mental models associated with such a fundamental neural task. Growing new structures and myelinating them requires cognitive rehearsal as well as mental models involved in creating new circuitry. Resource Room teachers are, thus, given an unattainable challenge. It is clear that a short amount of time can never be an effective solution to assist children to pull themselves out of the lagging deficit. Stakes are high in a competitive system where grades are used for moving up. This added stressor militates against these already "lagging" children who tend to fall farther and farther behind.

Individualized Education Program (IEP) culture is pervasive in all schools. Extra resources are provided for lagging children. Children become habituated to being "pulled out" of regular Gen Ed classes and sent to Special Ed classes to practice skills that are lagging. In theory, this is a really positive opportunity that should have consequential outcomes for all concerned. In practice, substantial evidence points to the fact that neither children nor teachers welcome this intrusion in daily classroom life. IEPs can be shunned as a badge of failure. Sensitive children derive anxiety simply from the label. They feel that their ineptitude and failings are broadcast for everyone to see.

Children are constantly comparing themselves to their peers. A level of anxiety and pain thus attach to the motivational connection and impede important work that is much needed, but poorly heeded. That culture of anxious fear with regard to IEPs, test-taking, and cognitive competition is pervasive in schools (*102*).

What if building cognitive and small-motor skills were presented as a fun "gift" instead of a punishing pull-out? In this next section, we highlight how an ingenious method overturned negative connotations associated with interventions. Tapping into intrinsic motivation in a kindergarten classroom, we report how an OT amplified autonomy, mastery, and purpose to improve self-efficacy, academic outcomes, and small-motor skills. This was a case of Theory into Practice.

Intrinsic as Gift Box

Theory into Practice (TiP) is an important call to action that neural educators use to implement change from the perspective of a neural lens. The following research study highlights immediate results that can be expected when a neuroscience of learning attitude is introduced into schools. Learning should be, and in some cases it can be, a gift. An occupational therapist describes an implementation of a remedial small-motor skills task that literally introduced learning in a neatly wrapped gift box. Her creative intervention utilized all elements of intrinsic motivation.

With this innovative approach, the OT designed, built, and implemented an ideal cognitive, small-motor skills learning experience.

- ◆ Children loved it. All children improved significantly in areas that mattered—small-motor acuity, reading, writing, and problem solving

- ◆ Teachers loved it. The children were so absorbed in the "play" aspect of the intervention, they didn't treat the contents of the gift boxes like learning but more like fun
- ◆ Guardians loved it. When little Johnny is learning and happy in school, guardians are well pleased with school
- ◆ Principals loved it. So did superintendents and administrators, because academic scores improve. The school's reputation is broadcast near and wide

So, what did she do? How did it work? Is this a strategy that any teacher can borrow for their resource center?

Children in this study didn't have foundational small-motor skills to do even basic tool manipulation (e.g., pencil and paper). Frustrated by experiencing so many children left behind week after week, Dr. Trummert created gift boxes that contained (i) a small-motor component (e.g., hand-eye coordination), and (ii) an academic component (e.g., cognitive/abstract manipulatives with math and reading). She purposefully aligned her project with state standard requirements for kindergarten, and devised instruments to capture data—pre and post.

> I wanted to integrate reading, writing, and math and put together a motor activity that was fun and included academic components as well—all in one cute little box.
>
> (103)

Having procured dozens of boxes, she enhanced them with bright-colored gift wrap so that they resembled the real thing—a birthday gift from someone who loves you.

What was inside each gift box was even more authentic. She designed hundreds of simple but challenging math and reading trials that needed small-motor plus cognitive skills to complete. For example, in Figure 15.1, the child sees herself as mama bird and excitedly engages in the mathematics of addition in order to figure out how much food to give baby bird. Then, she practices picking up and holding a tweezers. The objective of moving material with the tweezers in the fulfillment of the operation engages small-motor acuity. Everyone wins. The mama bird is happy. Baby bird gets food. And the tweezers operator improves small-motor operation, while manipulating several numbers in working memory to solve the "how much food" problem. This cognitive load engages all lobes of the brain in the implementation of the task. What fun! Over time and with weekly cognitive rehearsal, the

FIGURE 15.1 Child as Mama Bird Uses Tweezers and Addition to Feed Baby Bird

children grew important neural structures and myelinated them so that their motor skills and mental skills improved dramatically.

The results of Dr. Trummert's groundbreaking "academic gift" experiment were astounding. Children's academic and small-motor skills were tested at the beginning of the school year and, once again, at the end of the school year. All children improved—intervention and control group. The surprising aspect of the study was that the children who "played" with the gift-boxes not only improved their small-motor skills, their reading scores improved as well. All improvements were highly significant. These children, who had struggled with small-motor skills, reading and writing and who were lagging sadly behind the control cohort, made bigger gains than children who didn't need to be pulled out of regular class.

Though this finding is surprising, it corresponds accurately to everything we know about orchid learners. We know that they can encounter worst outcomes or best outcomes—depending on *in situ* greenhousing conditions in which they find themselves. Orchids are not broken dandelions. Time and time again, orchids have shown us that they can easily achieve their potential when given support and care of a positive greenhouse space. Being defined by their "sensitivity to social context," they respond with ease to positive, "belonging" support. Their enhanced vigilance, which at times can cause amygdala hijack and reactive anti-social responses, is a positive acumen when faced with a challenge that appeals to their sensitivity. In short, these children, who typically flail and wilt in competitive, stratified spaces, excel and thrive in fun, collaborative, and non-threatening environments.

Intrinsic motivation is conceptualized as autonomy, mastery, and purpose. Clearly, aspects of engagement were primed in the gift box experiment because of the presence of these three elements. Though hypersensitive, these children who fall behind because they react to fixedness, routine-ness, and cognitive load in an extrinsic system, recover quickly, and ably jump ahead. Looking at the gift box experiment in a new way, we note that children will experience autonomy first when (i) they choose their gift, and (ii) again, when they open the gift and decide where to begin solving the puzzle. As they engage the problem, attempting to solve it with reading, math, and small-motors skills, they receive immediate feedback that displays their mastery. Finally, purpose resides in each box. It's the quintessential "Me Here Now" scenario for a happy child. Objectives revolve around quickly figuring out the cognitive component, which they implement by using a tool that includes a connecting small-motor component.

Teacher Talk

The experiment described here reminds us to embrace intrinsic motivation tools as a way to make content and classroom teaching style accessible to children.

What was Surprising?

I am surprised to find out that my classroom is totally rewards and punishment and I assumed intrinsic motivation.

What I knew but now see differently?

I'm excited, for the first time in a long time, about my teaching. I knew that punishments didn't work, but I didn't know that there were alternatives. Everyone else is using time outs and clip charts as well. Now I see that if I link motivation with autonomy, mastery, and purpose, it will be easy to change my teaching style, and it will be easier to keep these kids motivated.

What I need help with?

How do I shift my practice from extrinsic to intrinsic? Where do I start? Is there a formula or a strategy?

Simple Strategy

Set up an easel and flip chart in a corner of the room. Children can make a four-leaf clover drawing anytime during the day. The following exercise in bilateral coordination is important for all children; it introduces neurotransmitters for learning, makes visible intrinsic motivation, and children find it fun and inviting.

Bilateral Coordination

Staying with the OT theme, information regarding this motor skill is available in all schools (104). Children need good bilateral coordination for simple tasks like catching a ball or a beanbag, cutting with scissors, playing soccer, or riding a bike. Using a large sheet of paper, draw a four-leaf clover. The flip chart paper should be within reach for the child so that she is staring at the central starting "dot" and have freedom to move both hands in a wide arc about her torso. In this exercise, each hand does the same job. To accomplish this task, the child will use whole body movement while focusing attentional gaze at a central dot in the middle of the clover shape.

This clover activity should be one large fluid motion. Once the child begins the drawing motion, she should not stop or lift the crayon from the paper. Arm motion should emanate from the shoulders and progress at the same speed, distance, and positioning. In completing the task, the child establishes direction and orientation (proprioception) with reference to the body. The activity touches on several very important functional structures in the child's brain. It establishes connections, builds, and strengthens circuits.

The activity addresses a number of critical motor movements that are essential for success in school:

- Hand-eye coordination in different visual fields
- Promotes spatial awareness and visual discrimination
- Addresses left and right awareness
- Improves peripheral vision
- Promotes body awareness
- Promotes coordination with specialization of the hands and eyes
- Works on gross motor movement skills

The best part of the activity is the spontaneity and fun that it introduces for the child. Ask the child to sign and date her drawing, so that they can see increases in competence and skills over time. Post the end result on the wall near the child to increase the sense of belonging and engagement through their personal work.

Summary

Children who are obviously not "ready" for school can make fast progress with intelligent supports. Teachers can reduce opportunity gaps by recognizing that sometimes a child's structures are not yet integrated with brain lobes. We focused on just a few simple easy-to-implement challenges and strategies—but the main idea is that because of a neural edge, teachers are beginning to view children with mental models that are based on neuroscience and learning.

Vocabulary

Crossing the Midline, Visual Motor Integration, Bilateral Coordination

16

Greenhouse Teachers too

Neural Education course can quite literally change the lives of everyone it touches.
—*Laurie Donati (Elementary School Teacher 2020)*

Greenhousing is not a typical construct in pedagogy. We borrow the botanical descriptor because it works for orchids. By embracing a cognitive approach in the classroom, teachers are vigilant in detecting hindbrain conditions in their orchids that stem from need for survival. A perspective about greenhousing constitutes *the* primary paradigm shift that is envisioned when teachers become neural educators. Most teachers are not taught about greenhousing when they receive their teaching credential. Yet, this concept of "supporting each other" first is an idea that resonates with teachers who spend their days on the front lines. Continuous up-skilling for solving crises requires continuous self-care. Children need at least four consistently caring adults to shepherd them through difficult formative years that are substantively more challenging today than yesterday. This is a Florence Nightingale moment in education. When teachers learn how to greenhouse each other, they are better able to greenhouse children.

Teachers consistently rate "immersive" neural institute experience as some of the very best professional development (PD) that is available. The catch phrase goes like this: "Managing the Classroom by Managing the Brain." In comparison with PD courses where they learn to "manage" the classroom with traditional rewards and punishment techniques, they quickly realize that this model is hands-down, streets ahead. The following statement summarizes what one-week working with other teachers in a neural solution feels like:

> I have taken away knowledge from this conference that will help me adjust my instruction in the classroom, my work with other educators, how I parent, and how I communicate with my family and community. Best training EVER!
>
> (Laurie Donati, Reading Specialist—Sawyer Woods Elementary.)

A deep understanding that comes from knowledge about pedagogy and neuroscience provides much relief with the answer to the perennial question: "Why is my child not performing? I know he has a lot more potential—I see it every day—but that does not seem to follow through in school. What can I do?"

Parent University

While guardians are usually happy to learn that there is a solution, they regret missing out on this important information over the years of raising older children. It's hard to blame them. Each of us has struggled through raising sensitive children in a rewards and punishment world that simply makes matters worse (31). Behavior criteria just alienate children from the very people who should be greenhousing them. Some guardians are upset:

> I wish I had known this when I was in school myself, or when I was raising my other children. How can we possibly raise or teach children and not know this kind of life-changing information?
>
> (Concerned Parent, 2019)

This statement sums up a typical reaction of guardians having attended a 90-minute session in Parent University.[1]

Parent meetings usually take place in the evenings to accommodate working adults. Here, guardians receive instruction regarding concepts and methods that align with what teachers are doing in the classroom. They learn a common vocabulary that supports children at home. Topics explored include functional regions of the brain (area for speech, for vision, motor skills, hearing, and so on). We also explore constructs that shed light on what teachers are using to help give children a working model about how they learn. Topics include: working memory, stress and learning, cognitive over-load, neurons that fire together, myelination, genetics, exercise, nutrition, amygdala hijack, sleep hygiene, attention, cognition, plasticity, intrinsic and extrinsic motivation, comprehension, focus, and creativity. While there has to be some theoretical information transmitted, the main focus is on practical solutions and hands-on strategies for solving real-world learning moments in the classroom and at home. Guardians derive value from concrete strate-gies for dealing with stressful situations, sibling rivalry, melt downs, delayed cognitive ability, and so on.

Guardians ask questions about challenging issues and seek clarification about the science behind items that are troubling to them: screen time, time out, punishments, consequences, discipline, adolescent experimenting with drugs, implicit bias, racism, identity, risky decisions, and more. Guardians tell us that they are pleased to spend the late evenings learning about real strategies that help them understand what is going on with their child's unexpected behaviors. They also state that they are in a much better place to provide direction and support for real issues in, and outside, the home.

The evidence is clear. When teachers and guardians do not have mean-ingful mental models about neuroscience and learning, there is diminished capacity for children to succeed. In addition, all stakeholders benefit from a deep understanding with reference to neuroplasticity as it pertains to mindset, intelligence, and talent. The underlying beliefs people hold about "talent" and 'intelligence' make all the difference when it comes to reticular activating system and self-talk. For instance, it's important that guardians and children truly understand what it means that "talent" and "intelligence" are malleable and modifiable, but not fixed (15). Without this knowledge, how can teachers help children who are stagnated in "stuck mentalistic" models that militate against academic growth? This is a "greenhouse" trag-edy, easily avoided.

Since humans are born with limitless potential, mental models that embrace this knowledge can enhance children's innate learning capacity. In this respect, evidence is again very clear. Scientists remind us to think "structure before function" (105) because structure determines function. This is a mainstay construct at the confluence of neuroscience with learning sci-ence. In other words, teachers and guardians can be intentional about grow-ing areas of the child's brain that are relevant for learning. These include a child's working memory and related circuitry that improves small-motor skills, mental processing, pattern recognition, and abstract and higher-order thinking. Children who gain successes in any of these areas are more capa-ble when it comes to self-regulation, inhibition, and metacognition (101).

Building and strengthening structures are natural outcomes of a learning system that is neuro-aligned and one that is intentional about preparing a child for future learning (69).

Research findings from ongoing studies highlight significant improvement in many areas relating to learning, engagement, sense of belonging (106), and happiness in school (107). Neural Education focuses on delivering PD to teachers on the front lines. Many who have already embraced a paradigm shift involved in a move to cognitive processing thrive with incremental successes as they learn to greenhouse their orchid learners. As teachers adopt cognitive methods, they change their practice by introducing nuanced techniques that are informed by the brain. It is inspiring to hear them report that, in their classrooms, labeling and stratification go away. This is difficult to achieve in a system that is so focused on grades and consequences, but obviously it can be accomplished with intentional practice and with affective mental models.

Parent University also describes a mental journey that feeds into the overall success of the method. When guardians and teachers work together, children excel. This is particularly accurate when they collaborate in a progressive model that includes common vocabulary about cognition, a mental model about neural plasticity, and a vision that interprets all behavior as communication. It's a simple truth: the more guardians know about the science of pedagogy, the more successful their children will be at managing their learning and achieving their natural potential.

Neural Education

Teachers who attend Neural Education courses are changed. They are amazingly quick to adapt neural nuances. They typically exit the course with several foundational strategies that transform classroom engagement. Inspired by the experience, they comprehend with deep visceral emotions the import of what this new approach can accomplish. Intuition and instinct play a large role in early adoption of a neural way of looking at things. Mental models undergo profound changes so that entrenched misconceptions, preconceptions, and accepted neuro-myths about how the brain works are made visible and debunked.

Teachers are not the best students. But in this case, they are already looking for solutions. The quest is for something that works, something that impacts the intensely structured space that they engage in every day. Many have become routine experts at their job, which they clearly decry as "upholding norms of the institution over the needs of the classroom." They see themselves as forced to follow systemic structural edicts that utilize social-evaluative threat strategies, which they know intuitively are not good for students (*108*). The sentiments of the following teacher summarize how teaching can be a reactive, negative place of self-searching and recrimination. She had come to the jumping-off place—a place that negatively impacts career trajectory and immediate self-worth:

> I didn't feel like I was making a difference anymore. I like to help people, and to me, nursing seemed like a better opportunity to help people.
>
> (Early Career Teacher, 2019)

Sadly, this is not an isolated exemplar. Data shows that upwards of 44% new teachers leave the field within five years—a higher number than ever before (*109*). At the same time, enrollment in teacher preparation programs is down by 35% in recent years. And as the workforce shrinks, those who stay are asked to shoulder additional burdens: Most teachers spend an average of $459 of their own money each year on supplies, with teachers in high-poverty schools spending even more, while 18% work a second job.

Instead of giving up in frustration and burnout, many teachers reinvent themselves. What a relief to build a new and inspiring future by adding a cognitive lens to the toolbox. Many come to this crossroads after years of trying strategy after strategy in a behaviorist world, and are expressly happy to finally make a solid breakthrough. By contrast, others express a strange mixture of frustration and relief when they blink and see the world through their sharpening vision:

> How could I have missed this before? It doesn't make sense that I would have spent all this time in the classroom but never think about working memory, plasticity, or long-term potentiation. This is truly amazing!"
>
> (*69*)

Teacher experience is in stark contrast to other stakeholders who inhabit the same learning arena. Government agencies, local education bodies, and many philanthropic funders are less adaptable.

The rest of the world pretty much embraces the long-entrenched system of rewards and punishments. Or so it seems. It has taken a long time (and there are still many "nay-sayers") to realize the connection between prisons, homelessness, and suicides and a rewards and punishments system that "pushes" children out (45). A paradigm shift from traditional learning spaces to a model that involves neuroscience is too removed from the familiar routines. Deep entrenchment in accepted systemic thinking can result in stagnation. Figure 16.1 is a clear example of data that is ignored over many years—data that clearly shows that American educational models are on the wrong track. Teachers say that many decision makers are too far removed from the front lines where subtle nuance can highlight the critical difference.

Confusion reigns in the learning space—and with so many hard dollars involved, people are cautious about change. Indeed, wealthy donors have tried to impact learning for many decades. They have thrown billions of dollars at a "broken" system (110), but as evidenced year over year in annual reports, to little avail (61). In truth, there has not been any observable improvement in American education since data was first collected (e.g., NAEP, NCES) around the middle of the last century (6, 7). This is more than disconcerting (111).

Change occurs in a deeply visceral way. Take, for instance, the description of a neural educator compared to a traditional teacher in the field. How would a neural educator differ from a traditional rewards/punishment teacher?

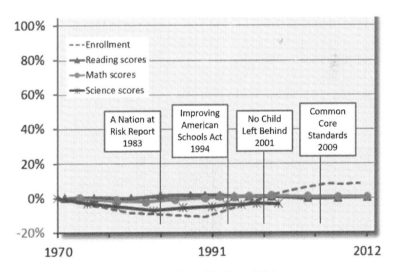

FIGURE 16.1 NAEP 40-Year Trend: Reading, Math, and Science

- When a teacher is thinking about strategies for improving long-term potentiation, she is not planning detention or figuring out how to manage behaviors
- When a teacher interprets a child's "unexpected" behavior as an indication of impaired working memory, she is apt to pull a strategy related to the neurotransmitter oxytocin out of her tool bag

These strategies deliver different outcomes for student, teacher, and guardian. Immediate outcomes for children occur when a shift is made from old-fashioned "classroom management" to a nuanced "managing the brain." Teachers focus on growing neural circuits, enhancing myelination, and flooding synapses with appropriate neurotransmitters? Teacher outcomes are described differently:

- **Professional Realignment: Teachers re-engage with "roots" of their calling**
- **Greenhousing: Teachers are not alone as they step into a vibrant learning model that changes the learning and teaching landscape**
- **Personal Freedoms: Teaching with brain frees up time, mitigates stressors, delivers happy learners, and grateful guardians**

Professional Realignment

Teachers typically enter the profession with a compelling desire to make a difference—a contribution to a new generation. Neural Educators reconnect to their professional calling in a way that is powerful and tangible. Teachers say that they "live" to witness light bulbs ignite for young learners, to shepherd children to a place where they can experience success in life, and contribute to society. Reality is much starker—data show that most teachers experience frustration and burnout in their early years (*109*). Four out of five teachers report that they did not feel like their first year of teaching was successful. They report feeling isolated, lacking mentorship, and have negative feelings about continuing with the profession (*112*). Many new teachers succumb to disillusionment and frustration caused by systemic constraints.

Greenhousing

Neural Educators are part of a dedicated community of like-minded practitioners—a groundswell of colleagues who actively advance an exciting new field for teaching and learning. It is easy to see a valuable career track in this arena. Teachers who make rapid strides in helping children that were previously struggling experience a reinvigoration of their purpose together with refreshed motivation (*109*). This, in turn, instills a passion and a new personal connection to their profession by simply shifting their lens from progressive punitive systems to neural circuits, myelination, and neurotransmitters.

Personal Freedoms

Finally, when teachers gain even a modicum of proficiency with neuro-pedagogical methods and models, they realize how accessible the art of teaching truly is. Lesson plans are easily distributed across boundaries since they were built to fit a shared model. Open education resource (OER) sharing within an active community, which is not vying to monetize their trust, diminishes any sense of isolation and bolsters strong pillars of equanimity and equity. They discover that they have a lot more free time for themselves, more success in their classroom and, most important, happier children. Their days are free of stressors that used to cripple them; classroom contact is uplifting, and the pleasure of meaningful work is evident.

Vocabulary

Mental Models, Parent University, Greenhousing

Note

1. Parent University originated in Seattle in 2020, when *Neural Education* defined curricular and practical activities to align parent mental models with teachers and their children's school methods that are implemented through a neural lens.

17

Autonomy Loves Choice

Bouncing is what Tiggers do best . . .

—*Winnie the Pooh*

No one said it would be easy to implement intrinsic motivation in an extrinsic world. In this chapter, we present a practical example of how we achieve it every time. Teachers are willing. "We just need strategies." This is the typical ask from teachers who are struggling to get past the rewards and punishment malaise. Asking for strategies is like paddling up the face of Niagara. Won't work. Strategies are extrinsic facing. For intrinsic motivation to take root in a classroom, it requires not strategies, but a mental shift. A neural shift is a mindset; it is an adaptive expert who understands the difference between adaptive and routine.

Going intrinsic requires living intrinsic. It's not something you do in your classroom; you must live it at home, in your car, with your own children. In other words, when we know how powerful the notion of plasticity is, how easy it is to create long-term potentiation, and, how amenable structures are to growth, we are not looking for strategies. We are implementing a way of thinking, a method that is implicit in the filters that come with cognitivist thinking. To know if you are being intrinsic right now, ask yourself: "What would I do differently, if I was using a neural lens in my teaching practice?"

Bounce a Couple of Balls

So, bounce two balls. Begin the journey. Don't allow RAS to whisper, "I can't do that!" It might seem counterintuitive—that something as simple as bouncing two balls helps a child become a better student and enhance capacity to reach full potential. Thousands of teachers are learning each day that it is, in fact, as simple as that.

Cognitive-facing teachers are realizing successes in classrooms with students who had a reputation about their non-involvement in learning. Such students were notorious because they couldn't follow instructions, couldn't sit still, couldn't focus, pay attention, were aggressive, and disruptive. These "bad behaviors" guaranteed trouble. Solutions didn't work—they were isolated in seats by themselves, received punitive in-school and out-of-school suspensions, and frequent visits to the principal. The same kids end up in the same unhappy place every day.

Teachers make subtle changes to mitigate the punitive chaos of classroom behavior. As shown in Figure 17.1, teachers are experiencing exponential growth in programs like Neural Education, where numbers tell the story. Since its inception in 2012, teachers have opted in, so those numbers have steadily grown from an initial pilot research study (113) to full-blown implementation across entire school systems in the US and beyond.

Several experimental sites are also showing amazing success. For instance, the Seattle School for Boys designed an entire schooling system

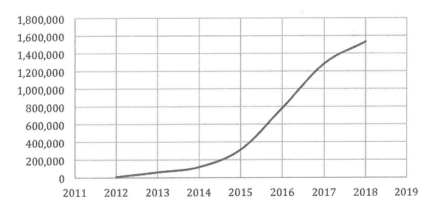

FIGURE 17.1 Neural Education Annual Compounded Impact

FIGURE 17.2 Seattle School for Boys is Designed on a Neuro-Pedagogic Model

grounded in Neural Education's brain-based pedagogic model. Students are expected to operate from a cognitive perspective. Imagine a school where there are no rewards and no punishments. Learning is a safe place where discipline derives from its true meaning—disciple. Figure 17.2 shows where children physically embody a cognitive approach to learning.

Children experience a process that is active, intentionally paedocentric, and especially aligned with active engagement through neuro-knowledge. For instance, in the Seattle School for Boys, students are active in three cognitive Rs—physically moving from station to cognitive station. "Reflect, Revised Thinking, and Report Out" are the order of the day. Cognitive flexibility, problem solving, and sense of belonging are paramount in this brain-based setup. All teachers plan their lessons with Miller's Law, Hebb's Rule, and Long-term Potentiation in the foreground. In this way, cognitive load, cognitive rehearsal, and structure before function establish safety for critical thinking.

Behavioral Lens

In schools where solutions for behavior issues are viewed through a behavioral lens, the options are very clear. Each disruptive action requires a corrective measure—consequence for poor choices. Children are evaluated in relation to their observed behaviors with a simple scale that labels them. We punish "bad" conduct so that behavior is not repeated. Punishment is a downstream event—we fail to solve the issue upstream, at the source. Why would bouncing balls be a suitable alternative?

Teachers are often cautious about trying something so wildly different. "What?! 50 tennis balls in my class?! Mayhem!" However, many teachers are willing to try something new, if they think it might have positive outcomes for their children. They will want to clarify a few things first. "Suppose I was about to try this ball bouncing caper . . . just say . . . I was thinking about trying it out. Which kids would an exercise like that serve?"

Here is a general list of what causes stressors in any classroom. We recognize these as executive function impairments (EFIs), and can easily match a face or two with the issues listed here. It is often impossible to teach while students are struggling to self-regulate with respect to any one of these items. At times, a teacher will be saddened when the same children get into trouble day after day with the same behavior. It can get so bad that a teacher will feel a little guilty on the occasional day that the troublesome kid is absent. RAS whispers in a consoling way, "I can actually spend valuable time teaching today."

Kids these days:

- ◆ Can't pay attention
- ◆ Can't follow instructions
- ◆ Are easily distracted
- ◆ Will choose something disruptive/distracting every time
- ◆ Can't focus
- ◆ Can't initiate tasks
- ◆ Can't stay on task
- ◆ Can't finish tasks
- ◆ Give up easily
- ◆ See no value in effort
- ◆ Are quick to say, "I can't, I'm no good"
- ◆ Are threatened by other kids' successes
- ◆ Can't collaborate with peers
- ◆ Procrastinate until it's too late—then paralysis
- ◆ Refuse to turn-in work
- ◆ Are anxious, worried
- ◆ Are argumentatively defensive
- ◆ Are a nuisance to others
- ◆ Are quick to react
- ◆ Are impulsive
- ◆ Are disruptive

A cognitive approach will produce results that are quite different. Behavior is telling. For neural educators, all behavior is communication.

Cognitivist Lens

"If I had an FMRI imaging machine in my lab, I could examine each student's brain scan and examine deficits. I'd know what actions to take to help grow the neural structures that the child needs for focus, for attention, for auditory processing, for verbal acuity, and so on. But, I can't afford an FMRI machine. I do the next best thing. I interpret their behaviors through my neural filters. When a child is acting up, or acting out, or just plain being silly, I am thinking to myself: 'Aha, Mary is in an amygdala hijack today, so I will need to increase serotonin and oxytocin for her. I will ask her to lead a brain-break that I know will fill all my students' synapses with neurotransmitters that help them learn.'"[1]

You can bounce balls with all children regardless of skill level or age. For instance, if I am working with a 13-year-old girl who is also on the school lacrosse team, I will have expectations that spring from that knowledge. However, if I am working with a younger grade, I might begin with a bean-bag before moving to bouncy balls. The beanbag makes life easier for small fingers, and her parietal small-motor center that is probably just getting wired. Beanbags are easy to hold and, if dropped, won't disappear quickly beneath a desk or a chair. This removes a level of frustration and distraction that allows the child to focus on mastery: catching and throwing.

Bouncing Balls

Instructions printed here are predicated upon some simple assumptions. We assume that you are working with children who are middle school age, give or take. It is fair to say that children in this age group are able to hold a ball in each hand and understand simple instructions. For instance, when a child is asked to begin with the dominant hand, they will easily translate that into either right- or left-handedness. There are as many ways to be accomplished at these exercises as there are individuals attempting them. We offer just one method to get started. We further assume that the teacher will make adjustments, as needed, to suit the age and agility of the children. It is very common that children progress quickly and soon begin to invent new challenges that increase both their fun factor and cognitive load.

Greenhouse teachers first. Before we teach children, we need to experience successful ball bouncing ourselves first. As shown in Figure 17.3, teachers express neurotransmitters in a fun exercise game of anticipation, focus, and attention. Take time to become proficient at bouncing two balls. Practice crossing the midline by catching the balls on the way back "crisscross" fashion. This simply means that you retrieve the left ball with the right hand and the right ball with the left hand. Begin with small groups and practice making

FIGURE 17.3 Teachers Release Focus and Attention: Neurotransmitters with Two Balls

up rules as you gain expertise with the balls. A common play involves teachers in groups of 10 bouncing with two hands up to 10, then moving one ball to the left. Teachers move; balls stay. Try it. It's a lot of fun. This game is called One Ball Left.

Groups have fun making up different rules. Just note that each new game can increase cognitive load while the individual is still gaining competency with two-handed skills. An example of increased cognitive load might be any of the following:

◆ Count in twos up to 100; each time you pass a multiplier of 10 move one ball right
◆ Count in threes up to 21
◆ Spell the name of each person in the group; move one ball left after each name
◆ Count in French (or Spanish etc.) up to 15
◆ Count backwards from 100 in threes

Work with a partner to experience the challenge, the focus, the fun, the sense of achievement, the purpose, the mastery, and the improved skill. Active exercises deliver advantages for children; they work just as well for adults. Children, who are growing new neural structures, increase blood flow to the brain and strengthen connectivity processes for circuitry. Physical activity increases synaptogenesis through a process called brain-derived neurotrophic factor (BDNF). Older adults increase metabolic activity with similar exercises. As we age, we need to keep neural circuitry tuned to avoid deleterious diseases that crop up. Indeed, as we get older, activities like ball-bouncing work in our favor to keep us active, learning new skills, having fun, and activating good neurotransmitters, in positive social play.

Science Behind Ball Bouncing

Model for students: Stand with a ball in each hand above your head.
Conceptual Collisions: Think cerebellum and four lobes. Review a simplistic overview of the function of each lobe—Cerebellum (balance, coordinating), Occipital (vision), Temporal (speech, auditory), Parietal (small-motor skills, peripheral), and Prefrontal Cortex (planning, predicting, managing).
Cerebellum: To engage cerebellum, stand with feet firmly planted in strong workout position.

Occipital (vision): Focus on one ball as you bounce with your dominant hand and count one through five. Repeat with non-dominant hand. Peripheral visual acuity will strengthen structures in the brain.

Tempora (auditory and speech): Listen to the bounce of the ball(s), while at the same time counting out loud one through five. Intentional loudness counts. Shout as you bounce. Improves attention and focus: **ONE! TWO! THREE! FOUR! FIVE!**

Parietal (small motor skills): Grip the balls firmly. Bounce with enough energy that the ball will respond by arriving back to your grip. Enhanced coordination and focus over time.

Prefrontal Cortex (seat of executive function): Manage, plan, predict, explain, assess, and assimilate. Make up new rules as you gain proficiency.

Cognitive Load: Increase cognitive load when students have reached automaticity. Step up to a higher challenge, but always revert back to the safety of automaticity where working memory is freed up. Children will be impelled to concentrate while making computational calculation, counting, balancing, and managing peripheral visual space while bouncing in a rhythmic manner.

Lobes: In this way, you will engage all brain lobes and cause intentional activation in areas that are required for attention, focus, concentration, mastery, skill development, and higher-order thinking and problem solving. A few minutes of this activity each morning will change your class.

Teacher first: We recommend that you become proficient on your own and with groups of colleagues before introducing it to your students. It makes it a lot easier if you can demonstrate activities and maintain control of bouncing balls, while other people are struggling to stay in the game.

Safety in Rhythm: The counting out loud is a soundtrack to introduce safety through rhythm. Children's brains appreciate safety and a sense of belonging.

Teacher Talk

Teachers who have already experienced cognitivism in the classroom are the best source of ideas for advancing cognitivism.

Teacher #1

So . . . first period today I had a kiddo all jacked up (over some-thing that would seem trivial to most) and my usual confront was not working. I picked up two of my lacrosse balls, stood, and start-ed bouncing them. I bounced one to him . . . eventually and (while seated) he started to bounce it. We kept talking, but the conversa-tion started to shift. We kept talking and bouncing . . . and I said, "Stand up and try it on one foot," slipped into the conversation. (He did). We kept bouncing . . . to one another, switching feet, each with two then exchanging, all while talking. During that 15 minutes, we covered why football was frustrating him, how he disappoints his mom, a girl he likes, and playing football in college . . . then all of a sudden he looked down at the balls he was bouncing and said, "I don't understand why this is working." He totally realized what was happening and kept bouncing! I explained the amygdala hijack and a few minutes later he was headed to class and had a great rest of the day.

Different schools and different teachers indicate how an exercise that is so fun and engaging impacts more than one person. Teachers greenhouse each other in the pursuit of experimentation.

Teacher #2

One of the students who visits my classroom has been working on the tennis ball challenge here and there when he comes in to take breaks, and today we got a good long round of the two of us bouncing balls together and it was fantastic! So much fun, so much goodness.

He was so hesitant to try the advanced—One Ball Left—game with me because he didn't see how it was even possible to do. He was stuck on the idea of both of us moving one step to the left . . . balls stayed behind. I showed him a video of other kids bouncing and having fun with the one ball left move, thinking it would help him see the possibility and he was like, "How? It can't be."

I said, "Let's just try it . . . it will be fun."

He was already really good at bouncing two balls. So, he took a risk.

He was so thrilled when we mastered the move—especially when we got a long round without dropping a ball or crashing.

"Wow, that is great. We did great," he was beaming.

He was smiling as he left the room—a better mood than I have seen in weeks.

I felt great too! And definitely more connected to him.

I hope he felt more connected to me, because he is in desperate need of feeling connected.

Colleague bumped into the student and realized the shift that she was witnessing. Positive RAS confirmed her belief—this was a case of a colleague bringing healthy learning neurotransmitters to this child. What better way to support than through cognitive play.

His smile was amazing. I saw him after he left your class . . . like a different person. He leaves believing in the possibilities of the day . . . and of himself. I had a good burst of happy energy after seeing him, too.

(Coach, Elementary, 2018)

Vocabulary

One Ball Left, Play, Dominant Hand

Note

1. Bouncing balls is only one of many other methods of helping the child learn focus, attention, empathy, self-regulation, and engagement. We highlight bouncing balls to start out, simply because it is showy, active, and is fun to do with a bunch of children.

18

A Lost Revolution

Sputnik moments cast long shadows.

—*Teacher*

Neuroscience came late to the schoolhouse. The fact that the brain—the one organ that is essential for learning—is not a prerequisite in teacher education programs makes very little sense. This omission speaks volumes. Teachers, in professional development courses, are quick to point out this gap in their preparation: "How come we don't know about Reticular Activating System?" "It's hard to believe I have never heard of amygdala hijack." "I wish I had known 20 years ago about the cognitive revolution with alternatives for rewards and punishments."

Indeed, many educators are surprised to learn about a cognitive revolution that, supposedly, occurred in 1956. Surprise turns to frustration, and not a little anger for some, when they realize that the knowledge contained in the so-called "revolution" could be beneficial in their classrooms. It was adopted by other academic entities—but not by educators.

The gathering of scientists occurred on the second day of a symposium organized by a "Special Interest Group" (SIG) in Information Theory at the Massachusetts Institute of Technology (*80*). It was at this meeting that George Miller delivered his influential paper on the limitations of working memory (*64*). Looking back, he describes the moment of conception as an exhilarating time "when psychology, anthropology, and linguistics were redefining themselves, and computer science and neuroscience, as disciplines, were coming into existence." (p. 141)

Without mentioning education *per se*, Miller admitted that it was a rather exclusive gathering. Referring to a paucity of resources, he suggested that many disciplines could not be invited to take part. Making no mention of the fact that education was not represented in the room that day, he did, however, acknowledge that, "Basic research in cognitive science has already had practical applications in such established fields as education and medicine."

Cognitive Science

In 1956, educators were otherwise engaged. Schools were busy setting up systems that were designed to educate large numbers of children who were required to attend school in the US. Figure 18.1 describes a summary of the state of cognitive science in a succinct graphical representation prepared for the Sloan Foundation. In this diagram, interactive connections and emerging synergies were apparent. It was exciting to witness groundbreaking new perspectives that cross-disciplinary scholarship might deliver to emergent and established fields—psychology, philosophy, linguistics, neuroscience, and computer science. It's impressive to explore synergies of erudite fields. The glaring gap was education. In an evolving cognitive world, there was no room for method, practice, or science of pedagogy. Already, academic scientists in other fields—notably psychology, linguistics, and computer

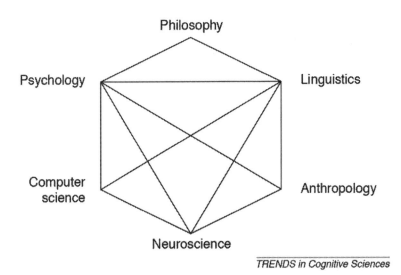

TRENDS in Cognitive Sciences

FIGURE 18.1 Education Was not Included in Cognitive Science, 1978

science—embraced the cognitive methodologies and were quick to "liberate" their fields from radical behaviorism with its attendant limitations (29).

Scientists in the room that day had no idea that they were setting in motion any kind of revolution that would eventually be known as the "Cognitive Revolution." They were interested merely in advancing the field of Information Theory by illuminating its connection with artificial intelligence. This is where a big pay-off for future collaborative research seemed to reside. As we listen to Miller summing up his conception of the future in cognitive science, we note the need to think about online learning, "teacherless" schools, and artificial intelligence in schools:

> A scientific theory of the properties and operation of the human mind can facilitate the communication of information, the instilling of adaptive habits of thought, the care for mental as well as physical functions of the body, and the development of more intelligent machines to serve us.
>
> *(114)*

Miller's theory had already outgrown Skinner. He shared Noam Chomsky's and Herb Simon's view that Skinner's ideations were limited. They began by disagreeing with his claims that language resulted purely from external sources. For Miller, it was clear that "grammatical rules, which govern phrases and sentences are not behavior." Chomsky was more direct. He forcefully belittled Skinnerian thinking by proclaiming:

> Defining psychology as the science of behavior was like defining physics as the science of meter reading.
>
> *(26)*

As theoretical scientists in emerging and established fields abandoned Skinner's theories in favor of a nuanced cognitive approach, they were deliberate about including mentalistic concepts. The brain had to integrate and explain behavioral data. Sadly, teachers missed out on this shift.

Consequence to Historical Change

That this cognitive revolution failed to arrive in the classroom might have something to do with the historical consequences of Sputnik (one year after SIG-IT-MIT), and the resultant existential focus on educational results and standards to ensure America's dominant place, ahead of Russia, in the scientific world. In retrospect, it is ironic that the scientific community, which had managed to sidestep "ruthless reductionism" implied by stimulus-response behaviorism, failed to disseminate their new thinking and methods (including brain and mentalist processes) to teaching and learning. The fundamentals of the very science that launched the modern information-age were somehow obfuscated to learning institutions. Schools were hampered with a two-dimensional remnant of the previous industrial age. Stubborn adherence to an antiquated school system relegated new thinking to prescribed learning methods and practices that equated learning not to cognitive processing, but merely, to memory.

Notwithstanding the reason . . . missing the revolution has proved to be a heavy burden for teachers. Education systems mired themselves in a 19th-century framework that did not fit well with needs of accomplished learners in an information age (98). Consequently, teachers have struggled to understand unexpected behaviors from discontented children, with commensurate lack-luster outcomes in academic performance (115). Further compounding the damage, this failure inflicted long-term losses on America as a country, where entire lost generations of student potential failed to materialize (14, 116).

By missing the cognitive revolution, teachers missed scientific "breakthrough" discoveries in related fields—especially neuroscience—that were not only meaningful for classroom instruction, but essential knowledge for how children acquire language, how memory works, and how cognition elaborates information. Educators were at a loss for methods, practices and entire frameworks that would have changed fundamental mental models for application of motivation and understanding in the classroom. For instance, behavior, instead of being 'bad' or 'good', would be addressed as an important communication asset.

As learners, we missed Donald Hebb's especially appropriate mental model about neurons that fire together wiring together (1960s). We missed Marion Diamond's groundbreaking discoveries about implications for enriched environments and neural plasticity through cognitive rehearsal and myelination (1960s). Neural plasticity is so critical for learning and yet teachers missed out on the classroom relevance of nuance related to synaptic plasticity versus myelin plasticity. We missed Hebb's critical understanding in relation to neuron assemblies (1960s). We missed Lomo's exciting discoveries, which implicated synaptic modulation and long-term potentiation (1970s). This opened the door to enhancing children's capacity to reach their true potential. If teachers didn't hear about LTP until 2020, consider the lost generations of learners who were consigned to grow up in a different paradigm.

Instead, teachers were asked to double down on progressive punitive processes that carried an innate potential to fuel a robust school-to-prison pipeline (14). Knowing about Reticular Activating System, we are sure that maladaptive practices exacerbated children's downward spiral. Could these negative learning events contribute to lives, which do not resemble potential? Teachers' lack of awareness with regard to critical information about Miller's Law is sure to cause cognitive overload for children who are struggling with formal schooling (117). Associated with cognitive load are issues pertaining to the size of working memory, the brain's capacity to create new pathways, the brain's ability to compensate for deficiencies, and the brain's ability to build strong structures for success.

In addition, the educational system as a whole was deprived of important mental models that are brain-based, that resonate with children's capacity to excel. Genetic and epigenetic factors are rarely in the classroom. Teachers cannot take into account a child's autonomic nervous system reactivity, or their individual susceptibility because of neurobiological differences to social context. How many children failed to achieve their potential because they were too sensitive to survive in a stratification environment that propagates 'social evaluative threat' (SET) instead of inspired learning (108)?

This is not just a sad list of whining teachers who are disgruntled because they are not very successful at what they do. Data reported by the nonprofit public policy organization the Brookings Institute describe the real story. Brookings data confirm a very troubling picture of our children in education since the 1970s. Brookings experts conduct in-depth analyses that lead to new ideas for solving problems facing society at local, national, and global level. The current US educational crisis constitutes a local, national, and global calamity. This is what Brookings experts report:

> For the nation's 17-year-olds, there have been no gains in literacy since the National Assessment of Educational Progress began in 1971. In Math, there has been no progress since 1990. The long-term stagnation cannot be attributed to racial or ethnic differences in the US population. Literacy scores for white students peaked in 1975; in math, scores peaked in the early 1990s.
>
> (118)

Brookings is not a lone voice. International literacy and numeracy data from the Organization for Economic Co-operation and Development (OECD) attest to the same crisis. This revered body is an international organization committed to building better policies for better lives. Their Assessment of Adult Skills (AAS) confirms the troubling picture we paint of educational outcomes in the US by comparison with other first-world countries.

> In the US, numeracy and literacy skills for children born since 1980 are no more developed than for those born between 1968 and 1977. For the average OECD country, by contrast, people born between 1978 and 1987 score significantly better than all previous generations.
>
> *(119)*

Comparing the oldest—those born from 1947 to 1957—to youngest cohorts—those born from 1988 to 1996, the US gains are especially weak.

The United States ranks dead last among 26 countries tested on math gains, and second to last on literacy gains across these generations. The countries which have made the largest math gains include South Korea, Slovenia, France, Poland, Finland, and the Netherlands *(118)*. These data paint a clear, if disturbing, picture. Over the last 40 years, the United States has invested heavily in education with little to show for it. The result is a society with more inequality and less economic growth; a high price indeed *(118)*.

Teacher Talk

> Each generation engages with their environment immersed in predominant worldview outlook so that energies and outcomes align. Historical consequences are very real. Generation after generation of children grow up and enter their worldview because of mental models and beliefs that emerge from home and school.

What was Surprising?

I am surprised that I never heard about a cognitive revolution.

What I knew but now see differently?

I knew that my students were not excelling in my teaching style. I thought it was just me. But all the other teachers were struggling also. Many of my friends gave up after the first year. Now I see that a system of rewards and punishments, a system of SET, cannot work for high Autonomic Nervous System reactivity children. And I had a lot of these kids in my class. I guess as young teachers, we get the "troublesome" kids. If medicine operated like education, the inexperienced new doctors would get all the difficult patients—a clear case of malpractice.

What I need help with?

I am working in a school that is driven by token economies, clipping, and class dojo. It never worked, and I can see why now. But how am I going to introduce change of this magnitude to my school, when administrators, the principal, and most of the faculty are invested so entirely in the punitive model? It's very disconcerting to know this information and not to be able to implement right away.

Summary

A century lost, or so it seems! Hard lessons in the classroom and out! High stakes choices with consequences that are viewed in the rear-view mirror. Teachers bear an inordinate load to try to implement a system that is essentially "un-implementable." We survived school; we should have thrived in school. Only time will tell. Will children who "actually" love to go to school do better than children who were coerced, bribed, and threatened with punishment if they didn't excel in school?

Vocabulary

Cognitive Revolution, Mentalistic, Sputnik

19

Maslow in an Orchid World

Especially in a post-pandemic world, we need a strong sense of belonging . . .

—Assistant Principal

Truly being seen is different from being seen. For the child in the room, it's about survival. "Am I safe here? Will the teacher do something unexpected that will make me look stupid?" The reptilian brain is screaming survival. "I am a sliver of a second from freeze, fight, or flight. These are spaces I inhabit every day. It's the only place I feel comfortable. I don't like it when teacher makes me step outside my comfort zone; I don't like it when other kids can so quickly and easily show their insecurities and allow themselves to be vulnerable in public. Please don't 'push' me. I'm in the room, but do you see me for who I really am?"

"I am," is the attainment of self—what Maslow alluded to as Self-Actualization, in his simplified Hierarchy of Needs.

(120)

Most teachers can recall from rote that Maslow's hierarchy begins with physiological needs (essentials like food, water, and shelter) and ends up at the top of a pyramid with self-actualization. This makes sense even with a cursory, non-scientific examination. It makes sense that we need shelter and clothing and food and water before we can do anything else.

Maslow based his theory on personal observations of individuals who he considered to be "self-actualized." Self-actualized is an interesting construct. When a student reaches the fulfillment of talent and potential, then they are thought to have "actualized" into "self." Finding "self" is considered to be a fundamental drive of our species, and indeed a stated aim for most educational systems: to achieve full potential. So why, then, do children leave so much potential on the table? Could it be that Maslow's "personal observations" do not tell the full story?

The science of situational anxiety includes fear, neglect, abuse, and trauma. It reveals a more nuanced story. While Maslow's theoretical work was useful for initiating research into the field of human motivation, his findings fall woefully short of scientific rigor for application in the modern classroom.

The traditional view of Maslow's theory is reflected in Figure 19.1. For an individual to become "actualized," Maslow offers a simple journey, implying a causal link: one has to complete lower essentials before attaining higher functions. Primary needs begin with "physiological" essentials; above that he advocates for "safety;" next come "love and belonging;" above that he places "esteem," and finally, having achieved all other needs, the successful adult attains "self-actualization." Maslow doesn't take into account the dichotomous sensitivity that teachers face every day with regard to resilience.

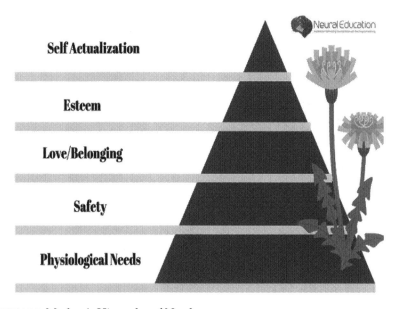

FIGURE 19.1 Maslow's Hierarchy of Needs

The observation we made earlier in relation to behaviorist classroom practices like labeling, stratification, clipping, token economies, and so on apply also to Maslow's work. His traditional hierarchical list appears to work ok for about 50% of students whose natural resilience will override negative impacts in a classroom where "love" and "sense of belonging" are not primary. For this reason, Maslow, like Skinner, is surrounded by confusion and misunderstandings.

More recent scientific research in the field of child development and readiness to learn reveals a more nuanced understanding of human needs. Evidence of structural maladjustment informs a more connected view of needs, which may not even be hierarchical. For instance, a child who is hardwired from birth to be sensitive (72) will require a reshuffling of the elements of the traditional hierarchy—so that "love" and "sense of belonging" come first (121). Figure 19.2 replaces the traditional model by focusing on the needs of sensitive Orchid Children. This in no way abandons the Dandelion Child. Focusing on the orchid opens up a welcoming world for resilient children also because all children need "love" and "sense of belonging" to thrive.

Furthermore, when a cognitive view is introduced to motivation studies, we expose a critical connection that has import for teacher-student

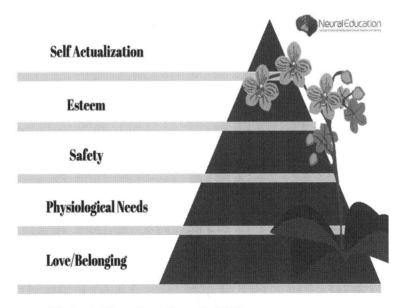

FIGURE 19.2 Maslow's Hierarchy with an Orchid Lens

relationships. New research reflects the intimate connection between the child's innate capacity—the self—and the environment in which they grow up. Scientists in biological studies (75), cognitive neuroscience studies,(105) and learning science studies (122) agree that fundamental brain structures— the very architecture of the child's self—are grounded in experiences during early life. Animal studies (123) (e.g., the amount of licking an infant rat receives from mother rat) and human studies (106) (e.g., rocking, cuddling, cooing) agree on the critical importance of early experiences for the development and maturation of the mammalian brain.

A growing body of empirical data point out that infants require maternal bonding, together with physical and emotional signals in order to stimulate growth. "Failure to Thrive" (37) is a consequence of neglect, lack of social bonding, and a deprivation of touch, physical rocking, and motherly pampering. Context can result in one child achieving high academic outcomes while a sibling fails to thrive. One child graduates with 4.0, the other is aggressive, destructive, self-defeating, and disruptive. The following account summarizes a mother's quest for understanding in relation to her children and grandchild:

Motherly Instinct With Science

As a mom of four, I couldn't understand why one son could be so different from the others. All were raised in the same household with the same environment. Listening to you talk about genetic and epigenetic effects and how hard-wired our autonomic nervous system reactivity is, I couldn't stop crying. I now know what it means to be hardwired to be sensitive.

And this is helpful, now that I am raising my Orchid Child's autistic daughter—also an orchid.

My 4-year-old granddaughter is on the spectrum. She has had a difficult life—suffered severe neglect from the beginning. Since she has difficulty communicating; we wanted her to learn sign language. But we failed.

The therapist instructed me to bring her to the outpatient therapy hungry. "Do not give her food or drink until she makes the sign for eat and drink." I did what she asked. My granddaughter just screamed and fought . . . we made no progress. She even refused to eat. I now know her brain was shut down—amygdala hijack—she was in survival mode.

After attending your training, I decided to try a different approach—based on how you readjusted Maslow's Hierarchy to put love and sense of belonging first. Oxytocin! I remembered what you said—it inhibits aggression.

I knew that she felt safer at home than anywhere else. So I cooked a favorite meal. After she ate, I kept her attention with a favorite game. In that game, we did lots of physical activity making sure she crossed the midline—because that is what you said to do.

Afterwards, I sat down and offered her a nice snack and her favorite drink. I knew by her response that she understood the sign that I was making. Within three days she began—used the sign for "eat," for "drink," and many more. Once she started, the floodgates opened. A few weeks later, we moved on to picture books.

I feel empowered because I now know how I can help her learn and communicate. Some of this feels very intuitive but I appreciate so much knowing the science behind why something works or why something will not work. (NC, 2019)

This account is from a mother who was able to schematize an understanding of how one of her children was "so different (124)." As a grandmother, she was able to "pick up the pieces" and break the cycle in "poverty in parenting" to overcome generational grief.

All babies are born with the functions of stress response already intact. In other words, the infant has a well-developed primitive brain that can react to stress, neglect, and other deprivations. This primitive brain interprets signals from inside and outside the body. It seeks love, affection, sense of belonging, and warm maternal touching that will nurture and care for its emotional and physical growth. The neurodevelopmental organizational architecture will shape in direct response to the physical/sensory input—love, affection, and sense of belonging versus fear, stress, and neglect.

What does this mean for me in my classroom? Why should I care if the infant brain is born with a well-developed primitive brain (hindbrain), a poorly developed emotional brain (limbic system), and a slowly developing executive function (forebrain)? Children reflect the world they live in. Their cognitive, social, emotional, and behavioral capacity is dictated by that world. The 5-year-old who is screaming profanities at the teacher didn't just make that up. Such a child has already lived a lifelong history of abuse, neglect, and chaos. Sometimes, the schoolroom is the only safe place for the child. That is why knowledge about a child's primitive brain has particular meaning for me in my classroom. Experience in early life determines core neurobiology. Dr. Perry, Senior Fellow at the Child Trauma Academy, sums it up succinctly (*125*):

> The amazing capacity of the human brain to develop in a "use-dependent" fashion—growing, organizing, and functioning in response to developmental experience—means that the major modifier of all human behavior is experience.
>
> (p. 2)

Teachers understand plasticity. They are familiar with the concept that basic neural structures are architected and strengthened with cognitive rehearsal. They also know that throughout life, a person's brain can shape with respect to environmental stimuli (*126*). However, there is a difference between plasticity for an adult who decides to learn a new language and plasticity for an infant who is setting up architectural infrastructure for life. If the infant has adverse experiences, it follows that basic organizational makeup connecting the primitive brain with the cortical brain will be damaged—a factor that will show up in the classroom.

From a neurodevelopmental point of view, the primitive lower brain develops first. Sequential development is the order of the day. Begin at the bottom and back, then work towards the top and front—hindbrain, midbrain, and forebrain. It's as if your classroom was a collection of very finely tuned amygdalae—keenly primed to react, fight, and flight. With careful attending, love and support, and emotional stability, it is possible to grow the higher-order thinking brain. This is where the neural educator will co-regulate with mirror neurons, using neurotransmitters that produce social bonding, play, and fun, to model inhibition, empathy, and self-regulation.

Intentional engagement with higher-order executive brain helps modulate and shape the reactive, primitive brain. From the brain's perspective, establishing that modulation imperative from the cortical brain, via the limbic brain, is the reason that it takes 25 years to raise a child. This is also the primary function of parenting, and why school is so important for social and emotional maturation. Dr. Perry points out the obvious (*125*):

> Any disruption of development, which either "overdevelops" the midbrain and brainstem or "under-develops" the limbic and cortical areas, will result in an imbalance in the Cortical Modulation ratio, predisposing to aggressive and violent behavior.
>
> (p 17)

Teacher Talk

Too often, information is overwhelming, fire hosed, and inaccessible—mile wide, inch deep. In this section, we strive to make relevant new research and data available so that you can choose to adapt as needed. The three scaffolding questions make visible what other teachers are struggling with, what they are adjusting to, and what they need help with, as we deepen our understanding.

What was Surprising?

I am surprised that a child's physiological makeup is so clear-cut and simple. I guess I hadn't thought about it before. I was surprised to learn how pervasive neglect and abuse is. It is hard for me to think of not loving and caring for an infant.

What I knew but now see differently?

I knew that the child's brain was malleable and that there were certain "critical periods" or windows of opportunity for development, but now I understand that plasticity is different for children versus adults. We are all shaped by environment—but what I see different is that a child is still forming structures, still building architecture, the very infrastructure of what the child will be able to do in life, whereas the adult is simply reorganizing structures that are already built. I hadn't thought about it as a mold, a kind of blueprint that lays down the architectural building blocks of what the child will become. I knew that stress had negative consequences for the learning brain, but now I see that I can contribute to that in my lesson if I am not mindful of the "Me Here Now" for every child. I now know what "teach to the orchid" means.

What I need help with?

Shifting "sense of belonging" down to where physiological needs used to be is massive. That changes everything I do in the classroom. My priorities must shift. This work has exposed many of the belief systems that teachers use for classroom management. Many are unstable, faulty, or based on myths. This is a worrying trend. What else is there?

Summary

When teachers explain their work as facilitating the modulation of the child's cortical brain with respect to the emotional brain and reactive brain, then the teacher is in tune with how the child develops and how the human brain is put together. It is a far cry from a learning space that grades, labels, and stratifies. It makes little sense to reward or punish a child whose cortical structures are beginning to form. It seems a lot more appropriate to help build foundational blocks of a child's architectural edifice, which will allow them become what they are to be in life.

Vocabulary

Modulation, Sequential Development, Maslow Adjusted

20

What Skinner Did Next

Would you prefer half of a quarter pizza or quarter of half pizza?

—*Discordant Attentional Prompt*

Skinner never advocated for punishment. "Punishing a child," he said, "served only to produce escape or avoidant behavior that might be even more undesirable than the behavior it was designed to punish (25)." How, then, did punishment become ingrained in every aspect of learning? Was it just a strange quirk of history? Why would rigorous animal studies involving positive and negative reinforcement schedules end up in the classroom? Skinner was instrumental in shaping educational psychology because of his strong belief that all behavior is described with scientific laws. His legacy in schools leaves much to be explained.

Colleagues, who were not as invested in the process, came to Skinner's aid. For instance, Eysenck, a noted British psychologist, made reference to a mismatch between Skinner's rigorous research and its eventual application in education, calling it a huge "misinterpretation." Looking back to 1980, he was trying to make sense of Skinner for participants at a meeting of the American Psychological Association:

"Skinner was one of the most widely misunderstood scientists of his time," Eysenck concluded.

(30)

Skinnerian principles attempted to show that how animals learn could translate into learning models for children. In some cases, the translation worked as predicted, but when human emotions are added to the mix, things fall apart at the edges. Two ideas illuminate how a grand scheme of misalignment occurred.

In advancing Thorndike's first Law, Skinner, too, focused on *Effect* rather than *Affect*. Like cats, pigeons weren't feeling creatures that think! Unlike other contemporaries (e.g., Sigmund Freud), Skinner avoided the elephant in the room—the inaccessible "black box" brain. Rejecting any mental apparatus to explain behavior, he concluded that behavior must be studied by examining explicit interactions between an individual and the environment. In other words, he turned his back on internal mentalistic activations in favor of external stimuli. Stimulus and response expressed causality for learning. There was no room in a method thus formulated for social and/or emotional thinking. The key concept was consequence. "Do that . . . expect this consequence."

Second, since Skinner's idea of "negative reinforcement" was arbitrarily interpreted as "punishment," it was ok to use punitive techniques in classrooms to counteract "unexpected" behaviors. Similarly, his idea of "rewards" quickly became associated with grades and, suddenly, students are labeled and stratified via summative high-stakes tests. Even formative assessments, (which are ideally meant to help a teacher adjust pacing and content delivery) were used as "benchmarks" for impending summative stratification tests.

Classroom Management

Over time, classroom "management" techniques evolved as essential requirements of teacher training programs. Since behavior was interpreted as a two-dimensional response to environmental stimuli, solutions emerged to match children's transgressions. These "solutions" included rewards that mimicked life with (token) economies and grades, and punishments that supposedly mimicked life with public shaming and clipping.

When it became obvious that extrinsic classroom management methods couldn't succeed in achieving homeostasis—positive and negative reinforcement formulas only worked for some kids some of the time—reformers focused their change efforts on tweaks to reward/punishment routines. When one is stuck in a "sometimes" successful model, reforms tend to look like Band-Aid fixes to the poorly functioning components. Imagine this conversation at the planning board:

It's clear punishments aren't working—let's try zero tolerance!

Chasing reforms into rabbit holes is a fool's errand. Words replace learning. And words quickly lose their gravitas. Equity feels neither fair nor impartial when implicit bias obfuscates structural racism. When public policy and institutional practice are outdated, our neediest dependent learners are disenfranchised (127). Teachers are forced to be complicit in a corrupt practice that shamelessly deprives children of instructional time through corrosive discipline practices.

Eventually, the education Titanic meets its "iceberg" moment at zero tolerance. As a harsh reminder of what occurs when an outdated two-dimensional educative methodology manages our children, teachers are forced to witness horrific scenes when children as young as 5-years-old are lead off in handcuffs by School Resource Officers (128).

Police officers handcuffed an unruly 5-year-old girl after she acted up in her kindergarten class . . . three officers approach, pin her arms behind her back, and put on handcuffs as she screamed, "No!"

(CBS, *The Early Show*, 2005)

Other forms of restraint are prescribed wherever teachers are *in loco parentis*. What teacher signs up for that trauma? Teachers, too, express real fears for an impending Titanic moment, or pandemic moment, or some other gut-wrenching moment for what could go wrong (108).

Schools must shift as a consequence to historical change. Systemic need for efficiencies do not diminish. New challenges deliver nuanced solutions. Solutions fossilize with time into institutional practice and public policy. For instance, we scratch our heads for the answer; it must be one of these state or federal interventions: No Child Left Behind (2001); Race to the Top (2009); Common Core State Standards (2010); or Every Student Succeeds Act (2015).

Reactions

Was Skinner just another consequence to historical change? His particular educational model appeared in 1957. That was the same year that Sputnik appeared in the skies over America. Both events changed every American's world dramatically, and each influenced the other. After the shock of Sputnik's silent beep-beep, politicians clamored for an answer to Soviet ingenuity; they looked to the traditional solution for science and math—the nation's schools (*129*).

> Though Sputnik was a relatively simple satellite compared with the more complex machines to follow, its beeping signal from space galvanized the United States to enact reforms in science and engineering education so that the nation could regain technological ground it appeared to have lost to its Soviet rival.
>
> (*Harvard Gazette*, 2007)

Congress responded a year later with the National Defense Education Act (*1958*), which increased funding for education at all levels. The focus was on scientific and technical education. Skinner's best-selling publication, *Verbal Behavior*, came just in time to fulfill a much-needed delivery mechanism. Skinner became the means; Skinner became the method, and before we knew it, students, teachers, and everyone else were headed west on a behaviorist wagon train. In retrospect, it appears that a hasty post-Sputnik knee-jerk reform, unfortunately, was responsible for consigning several generations of American children to a motivational machine that was inextricably hitched to the ultimate extrinsic engine. Carrots and sticks ruled the next 50 years! The beast was released.

Being hitched to an errant beast is an entirely capricious experience. Change is hard in the best of times, but when confusion reigns about what works and what doesn't, meaningful transformation becomes hazardous. Because delivery mechanism and content are connected at the hip, reforms that attempt to reinvent the one (methods and practices) cannot work while cinched to the same headstrong engine (rewards and punishments). And, it doesn't work to introduce innovate and costly reforms, when everything looks like Band-Aid fixes to 86 billion cuts. Ultimately, reform efforts are lost in empty wordsmith efforts—purporting to engage children with "intrinsic" motivation techniques, while, each day, they are cajoled and threatened in dire extrinsic stressors.

Reforms

"Our nation is at risk." This startling opening sentence to the 1983 report of the US National Commission on Excellence in Education highlighted the crisis in two extraordinary, if unconventional, ways. First, it underscored the meaninglessness of words at a time that America had lost its preeminence in commerce, industry, science, and technological innovation. If we choose saccharine soothing avowals, maybe we can convince ourselves that all is well. Thus, the preface to the report soothes flailing systemic issues. Suddenly, 1983 looks so familiar in 2023:

> All, regardless of race or class or economic status, are entitled to a fair chance and to the tools for developing their individual powers of mind and spirit to the utmost. This promise means that all children by virtue of their own efforts, competently guided, can hope to attain the mature and informed judgment needed to secure gainful employment, and to manage their own lives, thereby serving not only their own interests but also the progress of society itself.
>
> (130)

The Nation at Risk was just one in the long list of commissioned reports initiated by presidents and senior executives from the US Department of Education—reports that, in retrospect, architected a 50-year chapter of stagnation and decline. This is the second interesting aspect of the generation of educational reforms.

With great conviction, teams of investigators and interrogators continued to deliver soothing aphorisms in the face of irrefutable evidence of a growing crisis on the front lines. Education was not only stagnated; it deteriorated year over year. After *The Truman Report* in 1947, a second presidential report occurred in 1956 with Dwight Eisenhower's *Committee on Education Beyond the High School*. This was quickly followed by John F. Kennedy's *Task Force on Education* in 1960. And then came George W. Bush's Commission on the *Future of Higher Education* in 2006.

Meanwhile, the country limped west on a rickety rewards/punishments wagon, which was pulled by a near-dead behaviorist horse. In times of extreme need, many adjustments are feasible for the wagon—but it's mostly impossible to change horses midstream (12). In retrospect, it appears that all recent education reform experience has been hijacked by enthusiastic floggings of a declining animal. Appeals to move faster, pivot more efficiently, and achieve more academic outcomes were hobbled by exhaustion, ever-dwindling tack, and ruptured lung (19). Even Sophocles (441 BC) recognized that flogging a dead horse was no good for man or beast. We have arrived full circle to the Antigone moment in American education—dead at the hands of her own father (131)?

That some of Skinner's method works for some learners is not enough. Knowing about autonomic nervous system reactivity, realizing that large numbers of students are hypersensitive, it is possible to disambiguate what parts of Skinner's model are not ok. As neural educators, we recognize children who are living in hyper-vigilance. We acknowledge their reaction to school as behaviors that are "expected." We are quick to recognize amygdala hijack where the child is coming from an involuntary reactive place of fight or flight.

Extrinsic Failure

Evidence about reinforcement schedules is clear. Research has consistently demonstrated findings in line with Skinner's theories for more than 40 years. It turns out that "fixed ratio" schedules are very successful in some situations. Rewards work sometimes. For simple tasks, those involving little or no cognitive processing, the higher the reward the better the performance. But the minute there is even a modicum of cognitive load, the exact opposite occurs—the higher the reward, the worse the performance (17). This realization about how ineffective rewards might be in school can be incredibly non-intuitive. We would like to think that the larger the reward, the harder children might work. Teachers experience reality in all situations—their words fall on deaf ears. "If you want an A just focus and apply yourself!" However, we experience the opposite with the same kids each day. The "operant" word in that statement is "same." Day after day, the child who is unable to focus is punished in ever increasing stakes.

Research from related fields confirms these findings (132) and are consistent across many different domains of expertise—psychology, sociology, biology, and economics (17). For instance, from the field of economics, piecework rate-of-pay reflects Skinnerian "fixed ratio" schedules with reportedly excellent outcomes. Employers describe high returns on investment. The higher the pay, the harder they work. In economic terms, piecework is defined as a formulaic, algorithmic set of rules—"if . . . then" psychological event, which requires very little, if any, cognitive load. The premise is simple: "If . . . you do this repetitive labor, then . . . you get this much money."

How does this apply to the average classroom? The only time rewards work is if the task involves no cognitive load, is mechanical, and simple. Think about this. The time you sent the child to the library to pick up a ream of printer paper, he was delighted to do this job over and over for the same paltry remuneration. And if you doubled the payment (whatever it was), you would get double the result. But that is not the kind of work we expect from our students.

Learning involves cognitive stretching. We hear guardians say, "We feel we need to 'push' our child, so that she can reach her potential." No amount of reward will work for pushing the hyper-vigilant child. This idea of "pushing" is merely increasing cognitive load, increasing the challenge so that the child can stretch to increase some academic outcome. Instead, what happens is the child goes into reactive amygdala hijack. Brain shuts down and student shows up in fight or flight.

Indeed, the same "fixed ratio" schedule of reinforcement works well for kindergartners—if the task is simple, routine, and short in duration. Routines translate to safety. This fits the child's developmental stage, which is typically transitory between concrete and abstract (133).

The research is clear. The reward system fails when the demand moves beyond a mundane, formulaic, algorithmic situation. It fails when the task becomes more complex, endures a bit longer, and requires a cognitive component to complete.

Teacher Talk

In this section, teachers share their practice and process from a neural output. Attempting to embrace intrinsic motivation is a way to make their content and their teaching more accessible to children.

What was Surprising?

I was surprised to learn that Skinner was in my class. I was surprised to learn that my classroom was not intrinsic. I presumed that my teaching method was intrinsic, but we use a "token economy" system in our school, so I am forced to use rewards and, by extension, punishments every single day. This is very enlightening for me.

What I knew but now see differently?

I knew that intrinsic meant that children should like to do work and think it was fun, but I now know that it needs to be scaffolded with three constructs: autonomy, mastery, and purpose. These are very concrete steps and will make the difference between me saying,

"Let's do this" and me experiencing success, because I follow these easy steps.

- ◆ Autonomy! It's easy to add choice for individual events.
- ◆ Mastery! It's easy to achieve mastery when we give the kids manageable tasks for success.
- ◆ Purpose! This comes with every plan.

This solves a lot of boredom and disengagement issues that I see with children who have no sense of purpose.

What I need help with?

What are the elements of the Skinner class that will work for my highly sensitive kiddos?

Simple Strategies

Species' survival is everywhere in school. Figure 20.1 is an example of a teacher attempting to support a child at work. When I enter my classroom and look at my students, the first question I ask is, "Does Mary feel safe? Is Jon feeling safe where he is seated?" I get specific, naming the kid and putting myself in his or her place with safety and fear as the driver.

Eye Contact

It's always about each individual child. I make eye contact. I notice that some kids have difficulty making eye contact. I go out of my way to let them know that (i) I see you, not in a threatening way, but in a kind, loving, and supportive way; and (ii) I see all other kids also (I am not just singling you out).

Advanced Strategies

Knowing something about autonomic nervous system reactivity, I realize that at least seven or eight of my 22 kiddos are highly sensitive. I am ultra-aware now that when I raise my voice to "remind" one child to stay on task, that

FIGURE 20.1 Species Survival Is in Every Schoolroom

I am impacting at least these seven children at the same time. They "take on" the reprimand as if it were directed at them. This is a big shift for me. I had not even thought about the residual SET on other children when I "redirect." I see my teaching as a matter of trust. If I break trust with a sensitive learner, I do damage way deeper than I had realized—damage that could impact her for the remainder of the class, or the week, or the month . . . or longer. Figure 20.2 acknowledges that each child has a Me, Here, Now approach for engagement. Tone of voice, body language, and demeanor regarding my subject matter count—way more than I had assumed. Everything communicates a message to the sensitive brain.

Summary

Skinner may have been a large part of teacher preparation courses in many schools, but most teachers are blissfully unaware of the legacy of a behaviorist model in a modern classroom. Stress, trauma, ACEs, in addition to the increased competitiveness and pace of incoming new data bits in a streaming information age, mean that we have to reevaluate the relevance of a Skinner approach to learning in the 21st century. When we disambiguate

FIGURE 20.2 Autonomic Nervous Reactivity is Individual

reinforcement schedules from motivation, and superimpose the neurobiological makeup of a child, we find a more sensitive social and emotional methodology aligned with practical constructs for success.

Vocabulary

Intrinsic Motivation, Fixed Ratio Reinforcement Schedules, Cognitive Load

21

Teach to Thorndike Affect

We gotta lead with emotions . . . our children deserve that much.

—*Personal Correspondence*

Before the pandemic, classrooms were set in stone—literally. A physical building, a physical classroom, with butts in seats. Blended was but an option back then—an option grounded in physicality. There was always a school, and there was always a white board with a teacher and rows of desks. Sometimes, the desks were in circles and, sometimes, they were facing the front of room where the teacher had her electronic hub for a smart board and a big screen TV. And for the most part, teachers taught to Thorndike Effect—Effect with an E. Classroom was more than a place of learning—it was also a place for prescribed discipline, zero tolerance, behavior norms, consequences, and academic outcomes. Effect—meaning results—was the watchword of schooling.

At the end of the second decade of the 21st century, a global pandemic achieved something that countless reformers had failed to accomplish from Plato through DeVos; from Aristotle's Lyceum, Comenius' Pansophism, Pestalozzi's Yverdun, Lowe's Payment by Results, and Horace Mann's exquisite experiment in Public Education. The pandemic managed to separate children from teachers. As Silicon Valley tech wizards speed to monetize emergent new "teacherless" paradigms, much of the genius and nurture that teachers bring to the table could be lost. "Teacherless, online curriculum" is the catch phrase for post-pandemic modernity. So what are we losing in a teacherless society?

Singularity Schooling

This is a singularity moment for education. Even if, in the past, there were online components to most classes and nearly all children shared their work in the cloud, the teacher was still the fountainhead of social context and psychological safety. No one planned to have children sitting in front of computers for long hours, attending to the business of assignments online for grades that don't seem to make any sense anymore. The following information is consistent with data that was collected by educators and observers at the Institute for Connecting Neuroscience with Teaching and Learning during the first four months of COVID-19 social distancing (134).

Many unforeseen effects emerged several months into this cultural shift. Some were to be expected and others were simply startling. Guardians, the traditional breadwinners and providers of safety—the implicit place for identity and familial bonding—were suddenly and without precedent plunged headfirst into the role of teacher and monitor. The background computer screen introduced the virtual teacher, but the adult in the room had to manage the child's attention to detail, plan for logging-on, and staying connected (physically and socially), monitor lagging skills, and "focus" for staying on task.

For the first time, guardians were forced to experience their child in a "formal" learning space. They witnessed children in mental "shut-down," children in reactive combativeness, and sometimes, their child became the class clown—"that child" with behavior issues. Guardians admitted, "Now I know what it is like to manage 20 of these kids. It's impossible." Guardians were forced to be the provider of content instead of the fund of psychological safety—a role that they had taken for granted. The safety of classroom routines and school familiarity was suddenly replaced with something that made no sense. Guardians were trying to be teachers and school was in the home.

As expected, resilient children were able to manage the added stress associated with the shifting sands of learning. But hypersensitive "orchidial" children struggled to find their place, their identity, and their safety. Even in the same family, guardians watched helplessly as some of their children engaged and handled the extra demands that were placed on them, while siblings wilted and withdrew into an inconsolable reactive place of fear and anxiety. These struggles manifested and were expressed in sleep and dietary outcomes that were unsustainable. Some children slept better, were less anxious, and studied with ease. Other children wilted under the added stress of learning in an unfamiliar home environment that was neither safe nor social.

Psychological safety was perturbed by events and surroundings. Children reported a certain discomfort with where they found themselves: a place rife with discontinuity, ambiguity, and uncertainty. Equally disconcerting were elements of online interface platforms, together with teacher inexperience with online presentations, and inconsistent WIFI access. This combination caused children to associate stress, anxiety, fear, and failure with online classes. They soon got "zoomed out," a new term added to the behavioral lexicon that included negative reactions like "act up," "opt out," "zone out," and "drop out." Kids desperately needed connection and sense of belonging: "I miss my friends. I wish school would come back." These were the same kids who a few months previously were screaming: "I hate school. School sucks."

Psychological Safety

There is a lot more to school than learning English, Math, Science, Engineering, and Technology. Teachers already knew this, but the constraints of systemic thinking around STEM and a canned curriculum kept the focus on content, not on social. A clear aspect of school is delivered through a covert curriculum that is implicit in social contexts. In this space, young learners figure out who they are, how to interact with peers, and how to survive group situations.

And yet, something emerged early in the pandemic that took people by surprise. Some children began to say things like: "I can learn easier from home. There is no stress and no pressure." These were the same kids who were often in trouble, sent to the principal's office, or excluded from class because of behavior tantrums. Was it because these children suddenly realized that they were no longer being compared to other kids? They were not being labeled in the classroom and stratified against their peers. Class manipulation and public shaming in clipping routines were no more. They were shielded from implicit negative social contexts—the Zoom zone shielded them from stratification and label.

Some guardians reported that their children were sleeping better, that there were fewer behavior issues at home, and that their homes seemed less stressful and much happier. Here was a twist in reality. Could it be that school had been causing high levels of stress that were spilling over into homes? Existing data seem to confirm these observations. The APA had reported a dramatic increase in stress for young people since the 2000s, with the average reported stress exceeding that of adults. Eighty-three percent of stress for kids was about school (*135*). This aligned clearly with what guardians were discovering as children are forced to stay away from school. Stress levels are lower, and sleep and diet patterns are healthier.

Teachers who used a neural way of looking at the world were able to create a very different experience for children in virtual classrooms. In this model, the focus was not on content but on context. Intentionality is key to providing psychological safety. From the point of view of the brain, the objective was not how much math or science can be squeezed into the child; it was about how the child can become ignited in the distributed learning space. The content is but a means to an end. Affect trumped effect! How is the child feeling, as opposed to how much information can be consumed.

Psychological safety is manifest when the child can access higher-order processing and rational thought. The teacher's job is then a matter of ensuring that the lesson is (i) inviting enough (because it aligns with the child's interest), and (ii) exciting enough to keep a child engaged. Foundational thinking about the child's motivation in an intrinsic place further ensures (i) a common and stated sense of purpose through (ii) autonomy and choice during the lesson, and (iii) mastery as a result of the lesson.

Strategies for Psychological Safety

When the teacher is active in growing structures that the child needs in order to process and understand any math/science content it changes the classroom. Content becomes a channel for growing the child's brain, for igniting amazing questions that excite the child's curiosity and innate capacity for learning. Here we describe strategies that successful teachers enjoyed during social distancing when schools were closed and children were home online. The focus is always on the child, not the content, and the end result is Affect not Effect.

◆ **Photograph-Postcard:** Picture of teacher (with cat or dog) and personal note to the child stating that she is thinking about him/her and misses him/her. Co-create a belonging classroom even via the web. Use USPS instead of email.

- **Mirror Games Online:** Have fun mirroring hand and face movements with single and multi-screen view of peers. Mirroring will connect with mirror neurons and grow empathy in a safe, inclusive setting.
- **Handwritten Note:** Send in the mail with the child's name on it. A stark reminder of the personal touch, the weight of the tangible artifact, and a warm comforting message it contains.
- **Class News Release:** A personal phone call from teacher with important information about other children's birthdays and life events (new sister or brother). Share dopamine and oxytocin with cohesion activities that are meaningful only to this group of children.
- **Music Friday:** Carefully selected class playlist for end of week celebration. Co-create the list with the children and host a fun party on Fridays to usher in a weekend break with gratitude and sense of completion. Music is strong social cement that causes cohesion and happy sense of togetherness.

Teacher Talk

In this section, we hear from teachers who are gaining familiarity with the notion that the neuroscience of learning is foundational—content is a path to growing structures for healthy brain development.

What was Surprising?

I am surprised to realize that I hadn't thought of novelty to get the students' attention. I am also surprised why I had never heard of "Me Here Now" as a thing. I can see how easy it would be for each child to feel part of, with a sense of belonging.

What I knew but now see differently?

None of this is connected to math or science. I knew that the context was more important than the content, and I can see why that is so. I can easily connect my content once I have the child in the neocortex. I was aware that growing the child's working memory was important, but now I understand how. The child's working memory is really small and can fill so easily—by things that I may not even have control over. But that working memory space is all I have to work with. It's a minuscule space for the child to gain a deep understanding of my subject matter! It's in my best interest to want that child to have full access to the entire processing power of the brain. And I can do that by focusing on a few simple things: (i) increase activation of the corpus callosum, and (ii) connect each lobe with the prefrontal region, and (iii) recognize when a child is getting into an amygdala hijack.

What I need help with?

I fear that I am the only person in our entire faculty that thinks with a neural question. How can I get this mindset out there? The vocabulary I hear in the faculty room (even online) has nothing to do with neocortex or hippocampus. It has to do with "good" and "bad" behavior, punishment, and discipline. How can I change that?

Simple Strategies

We present here some strategies that worked for a neural educator in her distance classroom online gatherings. This is an "intrinsic" space that is fostered by choice, mastery, and sense of purpose. Techniques that I use will depend on the context and the child, but from my online bag of tools, I might decide on "storification". In other words, I am using visuals, concrete objects, and imagination to engage children and keep them in their prefrontal cortex.

Storifying the lesson is a favorite of all children who can easily find themselves in the story. With colorful characters, students can relate to the many twists and themes that intertwine in the unfolding of events. Safety, inclusivity, equity, sense of belonging, and "Me Here Now" are essential ingredients for storification. It doesn't take much creativity to storify any theme, any topic, or any lesson plan. Another way of saying this: I am greenhousing the children one by one.

Advanced Strategies

Gamifying the lesson is also a fun co-experience. I can come up with my own games to get the ball rolling, but it is always much more engaging and way more fun when students co-create the games with me. I regard it as part of the intrinsic operationalizing that I plan each lesson. Each child needs to see him or herself in the game. How do I add "Autonomy" to the lesson? That's easy—just answer the question, "Where is there choice for each child?" It might be as simple as, "What color do you want to draw this artifact?" or "Where do you what to put this thing?", or "What time (how long) do you want to do this activity?" Each child can choose something that makes it personal and real. Just add one of the five Ws to the lesson plan—What, When, Where, Why, Who.

Next, I want to add "Mastery" to the plan. Once again, I want to answer the question, "How can each child increase a skill or knowledge in this exercise—small motor and/or cognitive?" As soon as the element of competition is removed and the child is only compared against their own skill or knowledge . . . then can we truly make progress without labeling or stratifying. This is easy to accomplish online. The positive neurotransmitters that are released for the child when we stay in this intrinsic modality will ensure that the child will (i) want more, and (ii) feel good about their progress. Thorndike was right: "When I do something and it feels good, I will do it again." Serotonin, dopamine, and oxytocin will flow into the synapse—the currency of learning—and the child will delight in their innate capacity for excelling.

Finally, the lesson is solidly rooted in a sense of purpose. When the child can perceive a link between the lesson content and authentic real-life situations, the sense of purpose is uncovered. Making it visible is easily accomplished with a Piagetian maneuver that involves a "moment of disequilibrium". Piaget connected conceptual change with disequilibrium. When something doesn't make sense to the child's conception of the world, her meaning-making will be perturbed sufficiently that she will look for solutions. Ultimately, she will want to assimilate new information to prior knowledge in an effort to rectify the situation. For instance, a child who "knows" that the sun comes out by day and the moon comes out at night will be surprised to, one day, discover that the sun and moon are both out at the same time. That discovery will introduce the "moment of disequilibrium" to the mental model about moon and night—such that any new information in relation the moon's orbit about the earth will be adjusted to accommodate her first-hand observation. Understanding is not only immediate; it is forever.

Summary

Teachers who have already figured out that a set of neural filters makes a meaningful difference to (i) their personal worldview about learning and teaching, and (ii) how their students show up in the learning environment experience life in the classroom—brick and mortar or online—with a neural and progressive lens. Connecting neuroscience with teaching and learning allows teachers to embrace Thorndike's original plan for education so that all children can learn with Affect.

Vocabulary

Storify, Affect, Gamify

Epilogue

It just learns . . .

—*Geoffrey Hinton, (2019)*

Today's learner is the singularity child with exponential potential. The world of learning and teaching has shifted dramatically since 2000. It will change even more dramatically in the next five years. By comparison, the brain of a human infant born in 20,000 BC had the same potential as any infant born up to 1990 (*125*). Twenty thousand years ago, the child would have some language, no science, no understanding of computers. Yet, she survived. Place that pre-historic infant into today's world and she could play multiplayer video games, stream movies on her device, read, write, and think in as abstract a fashion as any child. The brain is amazing!

Since the 1990s, large-scale advances in neuroscience research have brought the human brain into areas of everyday life that seemed unprecedented just a few years earlier. It began with the Library of Congress and the National Institute of Mental Health bringing a new focus to the study of neuroscience, which became known as the Decade of the Brain. Accordingly, several initiatives came out of that period that testify to the excitement around "a deeper understanding of human brain organization and function (*136*)."

Initiatives include the Human Brain Project, the Human Connectome Project, the BRAIN Initiative, and the Adolescent Brain Cognitive Development study. Because much of this work is made available on the web, teachers, guardians, and students are able to access detailed images and ideas that heretofore were simply not available outside certain rarified ivied halls in the academy.

The human brain weighs about 3 pounds and is responsible for everything from managing a person's blood pressure to riding a bike. It does this through a series of complex neural networks that send and receive information through electro-chemical messengers. Machines can do this also. Geoffrey Hinton, winner of the Turing Prize 2019, describes how he was able to achieve infinite capacity with "deep learning" by emulating the human brain.

> In the past we used to program machines. It was laborious and excruciating. Not anymore! Today we tell the computer to pretend to be a neural network with a learning algorithm in it—that's programming—but after that if you want it to solve a particular problem, you just show it examples. We make it be a general-purpose learning machine; show it examples of inputs and outputs. It just learns. All we need to do is figure out how to adapt the connections—because these networks can do anything. It's just a question of changing the connections.
>
> (137)

Learning science together with neuroscience can achieve the same kind of success in tomorrow's schools. We don't need the machine. We have teachers. Our students shouldn't be programmed either. With a neural perspective, teachers know it's all about changing a child's neural connections. In Hinton's own words he cast a challenging shadow over pedagogy . . .

> We are able to accomplish amazing things—the neural net that we created can do anything—with a few billion connections we accomplished speech recognition in any language in the world. Yet the human brain has trillions upon trillions of connections—so either you are using the wrong algorithm or you are highly inefficient.
>
> (137)

When we foster children in learning spaces, with no labeling, no stratification—learning is natural and real. The brain takes over. Every child is neurobiological in the learning space—hardwired to learn. Each brain makes connections, myelinates, and floods the synapse with appropriate neurotransmitters so that the student wants more. The human brain has trillions upon trillions of connections. Learning is what we do best.

Glossary

A

Action Potential An electrochemical wave, which travels along the axon of a neuron. When the action potential reaches the presynaptic terminal, it provokes the release of a small quantity of neurotransmitter molecules, which bind to chemical receptor molecules located in the membrane of another neuron, the postsynaptic neuron, on the opposite side of the synaptic cleft. The wave of depolarization along the axon is called an action potential.

Adaptive Expertise A broad construct that encompasses a range of cognitive, motivational, and personality-related components, as well as habits of mind and dispositions. Generally, problem solvers demonstrate adaptive expertise when they are able to efficiently solve previously encountered tasks and generate new procedures for new tasks. Requires an individual to develop conceptual understanding that allows the "expert" to invent new solutions to problems and even new procedures for solving problems.

ADD See Attention Deficit Disorder.

ADHD See Attention Deficit Hyperactivity Disorder.

Amygdala Central structure of the limbic system. It is involved in emotions and fear, and is responsible for changes in mood and emotions, including rage and aggression. The amygdala is important for learning to associate objects with reward or punishment.

—Hijack an immediate, overwhelming emotional response with a later realization that the response was inappropriately strong given the trigger; responsible for the freeze-fight-or-flight response that causes a person to respond to threats.

Arborization See dendrite.

Arousal A physiological state involving changes in the body and brain that motivate behavior and enable response to stimuli.

ASD See Autism Spectrum Disorder.

Associative Learning Classical or operant. In classical associative learning, one stimulus evokes an involuntary response (dog hears bell, associates this with food and begins to salivate; boy hears door slamming, associates this with angry dad and shivers with fear). In operant associative learning, a stimulus elicits a response as a result of the stimulus. (Child exhibits a change in behavior—studies hard—so that he won't receive a bad grade in school).

Attention   In cognitive psychology, attention refers to how we actively process specific information present in our environment. A process in which a person pays attention to specific information connected to attentional capture and working memory space.

Attention Deficit Disorder (ADD)   A condition or syndrome often described in schools for children who display symptoms of difficulty maintaining attention. Characterized by distractibility, impulsivity, and restlessness.

Attention Deficit Hyperactivity Disorder   (ADHD) A condition characterized by excessively inattentive, hyperactive, or impulsive behaviors. ADHD is often the obvious diagnosis by parents and teachers for children who have difficulty with attention, staying on task, or working with peers.

Autism Spectrum Disorder   (ASD) A set of conditions characterized, in part, by impaired social communication and interaction, and narrow, obsessive interests or repetitive behaviors.

Auditory Tract   Processing of auditory information, identifying auditory "objects," and identifying the location of sound.

Autonomic Nervous System   A division of the peripheral nervous system that influences the function of internal organs. Autonomic implies that ANS is independent of cerebral cortex and not subject to conscious control.

Aversive   In operant conditioning, a tendency to repel, causing avoidance of a situation, a place, or a thing.

Axon   A long, thread-like part of a nerve cell that facilitates communication. Electrical impulses are conducted away from the cell body to other cells. Although each neuron can have only one axon, the axon itself can have many branches, which connects it to many others. Myelinated axons are known as nerve fibers. The function of the axon is to transmit information to different neurons, muscles, and glands.

—Terminal   Site where one neuron transmits a signal to another neuron's receptors by changing the electrical signal into a chemical signal called a neurotransmitter.

B

BDNF   A crucial protein called Brain-Derived Neurotrophic Factor, which is essential for maintaining healthy neurons and creating new ones. Physical exercise is linked to BDNF production.

Behaviorism   Psychological theory that behavior can be explained in terms of conditioning, without appeal to thoughts or feelings. Only concerned with observable stimulus-response behaviors. Behaviorists believe that all behaviors are learned through interaction with the environment.

Brain   An extraordinarily complex and fine-tuned communications network. It has many folds and overlapping structures so that all its complexity can fit inside a human head. The brain consists of approximately a hundred billion neurons, and close to a quadrillion connections between them. From this complex mass, which typically just weighs 3 pounds, comes human consciousness and all our emotions and imaginings.

—Stem   Forms the connection between the brain and the spinal cord. Maintains vital control of the heart and lungs, and coordinates many important reflexes. The brain stem, through its gray matter, provides many of the basic survival and reflex functions for the body. Through its white matter, the brain stem forms the connections between the brain and the body via the spinal cord.

Broca's Speech Area   A region in the frontal lobe of the left hemisphere of the brain with functions linked to speech production. Language processing has been linked to this part of the brain—Broca's area—since Pierre Paul Broca examined impairments in several patients who suffered from aphasia in the 1860s.

C

Cell Body   The cell body (soma) is the factory of the neuron. It produces all the proteins for the dendrites, axons, and synaptic terminals and contains specialized organelles (E.g., mitochondria).

Cerebellum   Located behind the top part of the brain stem (where the spinal cord meets the brain). It contains roughly half of the brain's neurons, specialized cells that transmit information via electrical signals. It receives information from the sensory systems (touch, sound, smell, etc.), the spinal cord, and other parts of the brain and then regulates motor movements (walking, running, lifting, etc.).

Cerebral Cortex   The outer layer of the brain that covers both hemispheres. It protects the brain, and at 2–3 mm thick, it houses the gyri (ridges) and sulci (valleys or grooves). The cerebral cortex plays a key role in memory, attention, perception, awareness, thoughts, language, and consciousness. The cerebral cortex is folded, giving a much greater surface area in the confined volume of the skull.

Chunking A method by which individual pieces of information are bound together into a meaningful whole that conforms to Miller's (Cowan's adjusted) Law to aid in cognitive processing.

Circadian Rhythm A sleep/waking cycle that occurs naturally in the 24-hour cycle of day/night. Even though this biological clock is natural and built in, it can be impacted by environment and other external stimuli, and especially by light and temperature and food. Melatonin is a neurotransmitter that helps regulate sleep and wake cycles by anticipating the daily onset of darkness. Circadian rhythms are very different for adolescents and adults.

Classical Conditioning Automatic reflex (like a dog salivating for food) is associated (paired) with a meaningless stimulus (a metronome) so that the one stimulus elicits the response from the second stimulus (metronome chimes, dog salivates). Classical conditioning is limited when it comes to shaping behavior, because an automatic response must already exist.

Cognitive Overload Occurs when we reach the limitations of working memory. Too much information for the learner to process. When we reach processing limits of the learner it produces anxiety and stress.

Cognitive Rehearsal Used in strengthening and adding myelin to relevant synaptic connections. Mediated repetition and practice therefore help to reinforce learning. Cognitive rehearsal can be planned so that learners achieve a level of automaticity and routine that make their learning successful.

Cognitivism Stemming from the Cognitive Revolution—September 11, 1956—a counter revolution to behaviorist thinking in which mentalistic models are implied in learning that explain behavior.

Comprehension The act of grasping meaning with the intellect for fully understanding.

Consolidation Sleep benefits the retention of memory. Sleep as a state of greatly reduced external information processing represents an optimal time for consolidating memories. Theories characterize sleep as a brain state optimizing memory consolidation, in opposition to the waking brain being optimized for encoding of memories. Consolidation originates from reactivation of recently encoded neuronal memory representations, which occur during slow wave sleep (SWS) and transform respective representations for integration into long-term memory. Ensuing Rapid Eye Movement (REM) sleep may stabilize transformed memories.

Corpus Callosum   Essential to the integration of the information between left and right cerebral hemispheres. Each hemisphere controls movement in the opposite side of the body. The corpus callosum is the largest white matter structure in the brain, consisting of 200–250 million contralateral axonal projections and the major commissural pathway connecting the hemispheres.

Cortex   Cortex is the outer layer of the cerebrum, composed of folded gray matter. It plays an important role in consciousness.

Cortisol   Cortisol works with epinephrine (adrenaline) to create memories of short-term emotional events; this is the proposed mechanism for storage of flash bulb memories, and may originate as a means to remember what to avoid in the future. However, long-term exposure to cortisol damages cells in the hippocampus; this damage results in impaired learning. Furthermore, it has been shown that cortisol inhibits memory retrieval of already stored information. High cortisol levels have been observed in connection with abnormal Adrenocorticotropic Hormone (ACTH) levels, clinical depression, psychological stress, and physiological stressors such as hypoglycemia, illness, fever, trauma, surgery, fear, pain, physical exertion, or temperature extremes.

D

Dendrite   A short-branched extension of a nerve cell, along which impulses received from other cells at synapses are transmitted to the cell body.

Dendritic Arborization   A tree-like branching of dendrites that facilitate new synaptic connections.

Dendritic Spines   Small projections on dendrites that increase receptive properties and isolate signal specificity.

Developmental Psychology   A scientific approach, which aims to explain how children and adults change over time.

Disequilibrium   A state in which things are not stable or certain, but are likely to change suddenly. Piaget introduced the idea that a moment of disequilibrium would perturb a child's mental model about the world sufficiently to cause perceptual change.

Dopamine   A neurotransmitter that helps control the brain's reward and pleasure centers. Dopamine also helps regulate movement and emotional responses, and it enables us not only to see rewards, but to take action to move toward them.

E

Electrical Conduction   Neurons have evolved unique capabilities for communication between cells. To achieve long-distance and rapid communication, neurons have evolved special abilities for sending electrical signals along axons. This mechanism, called conduction, is how the cell body of a neuron communicates with its own terminals via the axon. Communication between neurons is then achieved at synapses by a process of neurotransmission.

Emotion System   Emotions are different mental reactions that are expressed by humans—happy, sad, angry, hopeful, and so on. They play a role in how humans behave individually and socially. The emotion system of the brain is also called the limbic system. It is composed of structures that deal with emotions (such as anger, happiness, and fear) as well as memories.

Executive Function   Mental processes that enable one to plan, focus attention, remember instructions, and juggle multiple tasks successfully. The brain needs this skillset to filter distractions, prioritize tasks, set and achieve goals, and control impulses.

Exercise   Physical exercise is not only important for the body's health—it is also essential for the brain to stay sharp. Physical exercise increases heart rate, which pumps more oxygen to the brain, thus enhancing brain plasticity by stimulating growth of new connections between cells in a wide array of important cortical areas. A link between exercise and BDNF is widely accepted. BDNF is a crucial protein called brain-derived neurotrophic factor, which is essential for maintaining healthy neurons and creating new ones. Physical exercise is crucial to staving off neurological diseases, including Alzheimer's and Parkinson's.

Extrinsic Motivation   Behavior is motivated by an external factor influencing a person to do an activity in hopes of earning a reward—or avoiding a less-than-positive outcome.

F

Fight, Flight, Freeze   A body's automatic, built-in system designed to protect from threat or danger—critical to survival from real danger. Problem is . . . for a lot of learners, anxiety can also trigger a fight, flight, freeze system when they believe there is threat or danger even if there is not.

Firing   A neuron that emits an action potential is said to "fire." When all synapses are firing, an individual feels focused and the mind feels electric. Neurons emit pulses called "spikes" that last about 1 millisecond. Each neuron fires (emits a spike) on the order of ten times per second.

Fixed Mindset   Underlying beliefs people have about learning and intelligence. Some people believe their basic qualities, like their intelligence or talent, are simply fixed traits.

Frontal Lobe   Each of the paired lobes of the brain lying immediately behind the forehead, including areas concerned with behavior, learning, personality, and voluntary movement.

Functional Imaging   Functional imaging is the study of human brain function based on analysis of data acquired using brain imaging modalities such as Electroencephalography (EEG), Magneto encephalography (MEG), functional Magnetic Resonance Imaging (fMRI), Positron Emission Tomography (PET), or Optical Imaging.

G

Gray Matter   The darker tissue of the brain and spinal cord, consisting mainly of nerve cell bodies and branching dendrites.

Growth Mindset   An underlying belief people have about learning and intelligence. When students believe they can get smarter, they understand that effort makes them stronger. When a person changes their belief from fixed to growth mindset, it leads to increased motivation and achievement.

Gyrus   A raised fold of brain tissue surrounded a sulcus. The mixture of Gyri (ridges) and Sulci (grooves) creates the characteristic folded appearance in the brain.

H

Habit   Habits are behaviors wired so deeply in our brains that we perform them automatically. Everyone has habits—some good, some bad. Habits come from a place of automaticity and free up the brain to do other things. A small region of the brain's prefrontal cortex, where most thought and planning occurs—the Infralimbic Cortex— is responsible for moment-by-moment control of which habits are switched on at a given time. Habits suggest an automatic, reflexive mode rather than a mode that's more cognitive or engaged in a goal. Studies show that the Infralimbic Cortex favors new habits over old ones—when habits are broken they are not forgotten, but replaced with new ones.

Habituate   A form of learning in which an organism decreases or ceases to respond to a stimulus after repeated presentations. Essentially, the organism learns to stop responding to a stimulus, which is no longer biologically relevant. Habituation is the decrease of a response to a repeated eliciting stimulus that is not due to sensory adaption or motor fatigue. The habituation process is a form of adaptive behavior (neuroplasticity) that is classified as non-associative learning. For example, organisms may habituate to repeated sudden loud noises when they learn these have no consequences.

Hebb's Rule   A neuroscientific theory claiming that an increase in synaptic efficacy arises from a presynaptic cell's repeated and persistent stimulation of a postsynaptic cell. It is an attempt to explain synaptic plasticity, the adaptation of brain neurons during the learning process. Neurons that fire together wire together.

Hemisphere   The brain is divided into two hemispheres, called the left and right hemispheres. Each hemisphere provides a different set of functions, behaviors, and controls.

Higher Cognitive Functions   A set of cognitive processes—including attentional control, inhibitory control, working memory, and cognitive flexibility, as well as reasoning, problem solving, and planning—that are necessary for the cognitive control of behavior: selecting and successfully monitoring behaviors that facilitate the attainment of chosen goals. Executive functions mature at different rates over time. Some abilities peak maturation rate in late childhood or adolescence, while others' progress into early adulthood. The brain continues to mature and develop connections well into adulthood. A person's executive function abilities are shaped by both physical changes in the brain and by life experiences in the classroom and in the world at large.

Hippocampus   Center of emotion, memory, and the autonomic nervous system.

Hippocampal Neurogenesis   Growing new neurons in the hippocampus region of the brain.

Hypothalamus   Literally means above (Hypo) the Thalamus. The hypothalamus houses emotions, as well as regulates body temperature, blood pressure, thirst, and hunger.

I

Inhibitory Firing   At chemical synapses in the brain, GABA (gamma-aminobutyric acid) is a transmitter for inhibition. The balance between neural excitation and neural inhibition is crucial to healthy cognition and behavior.

Intelligence   Ability to acquire and apply knowledge and skills. It is widely accepted that there are different types of intelligence—analytic, linguistic, and emotional, to name a few.

Intentional Practice   Purposeful and systematic exercises beyond mindless repetition. Requires focused attention and is conducted with the specific goal of improving performance.

Intrinsic Motivation   Behavior that is driven by internal rewards. The perception of an activity as an opportunity to explore, learn, and actualize one's own potential. Activated through autonomy, mastery, and purpose.

Introspection   The examination or observation of one's own mental and emotional processes.

Involuntary Movement   Reflexes are fundamental involuntary movements. All reflexes involve the activation of small sensory receptors in the skin, the joints, or even in the muscles themselves. These are relatively fixed, automatic muscle responses to particular stimuli, such as the slight extension of the leg when a physician taps the knee with a small rubber hammer.

J

Jet Lag   (see also Circadian Rhythm): A circadian disruption that puts us in conflict with our natural sleep patterns. Travel from one time zone to others over long distances will cause a shift in time and light cues on the brain, which forces the body to alter its normal pattern. This is why jet lag can leave travelers feeling sluggish. We typically have more difficulty thinking and performing physical or cognitive functions well. It usually takes a couple days for the body to adjust its internal clock in alignment to the local clock.

K

Kinesthetic Teaching and Learning   (tactile learning): A teaching method in which learning takes place by students carrying out physical activities, rather than listening to a lecture or watching demonstrations.

L

Language Comprehension An important aspect of day-to-day functioning in adulthood. Comprehension of written and spoken language relies on the ability to correctly process word and phrase meanings, sentence grammar, and discourse or text structure.

Law of Effect E. L. Thorndike (1929) carried out experiments with cats using a famous puzzle box in which he demonstrated that behavior changes because of its consequences.

Limbic Brain A part of the brain, which emerged in the first mammals. It can record memories of behaviors that produced agreeable and disagreeable experiences, so it is responsible for what are called emotions in human beings. The main structures of the limbic brain are the hippocampus, the amygdala, and the hypothalamus. The limbic brain is the seat of the value judgments that we make, often unconsciously, that exert such a strong influence on our behavior.

Limbic System A complex set of brain structures located on both sides of the thalamus. The limbic system supports a variety of functions including emotion, behavior, motivation, long-term memory, and olfaction. Emotional life is largely housed in the limbic system, and it has a great deal to do with the formation of memories. It controls the basic emotions (fear, pleasure, anger) and drives (hunger, sex, dominance, care of offspring).

Lobe Cerebral cortex of the brain is divided into four sections: frontal lobe, parietal lobe, occipital lobe, and temporal lobe.

—Frontal Each of the paired lobes of the brain lying immediately behind the forehead, areas concerned with behavior, learning, personality, and voluntary movement.

—Occipital The rearmost lobe in each cerebral hemisphere of the brain, concerned with vision.

—Parietal Either of the paired lobes of the brain at the top of the head, areas concerned with the reception and correlation of sensory information.

—Temporal Each of the paired lobes of the brain lying beneath the temples, areas concerned with the understanding of speech.

Long Term Potentiation LTP is referred to as a strengthening of synaptic connections between two neurons that are activated simultaneously. Pertains to memory and learning.

M

Me, Here, Now   Attentional aspect of learning; relevance and immediacy pertains to attention and learning.

Memory (Episodic Events)   Memory of autobiographical events (times, places, associated emotions, and other contextual who, what, when, where, why knowledge) that can be explicitly stated. Episodic memories include various details about these events, such as what happened, when it happened, and where it happened.

—Consolidation   The brain processes information that was experienced during consciousness by (i) consolidating memories that we want to keep, and (ii) getting rid of memories that we don't want to keep.

—(Long Term)   Information can be stored for long periods of time. While short-term and working memory persist for only about 18 to 30 seconds, information can remain in long-term memory indefinitely.

—(Short Term) (see also Working Memory): The term working memory is used to describe the process where one "holds on" to small bits of recently learned information. An example of working memory would be the ability to hold on to the digits of a phone number in the short time between hearing them and dialing the number. The capacity of working memory is limited, allowing us to remember only a few bits of information at one time.

Mental Model   Representation of concepts, frameworks, or worldviews that you carry around in your mind. Thinking tools that one uses to understand life, make decisions, and solve problems.

Metacognition   Thinking about one's thinking. Knowledge about one's own information processing and strategies that influence one's learning that can optimize future learning.

Miller's Law   A 1956 paper entitled, "The Magical Number Seven Plus or Minus Two." According to George Miller, memory span is not limited in terms of bits, but rather, in terms of chunks. His research defined the limitation of human working memory. Cowan, revisiting Miller's research 2001, offered a newer and updated limitation to working memory (Four Plus or Minus Two).

Mirror Neurons   Mirror neurons are neurons that fire both when an individual performs an action and when the individual sees or hears another perform a similar action. The discovery of these neurons has been very influential in explaining how individuals make sense of the actions of others by showing that, when a person perceives the actions of others, the person activates the motor programs which they would use to perform similar actions.

Motivation Motivation is the desire to do something and it's usually due to some sort of reward. It is a reason a person has for acting in a particular way or carrying out some action. However, we are all motivated by different things. Increased dopamine in the Nucleus Accumbens signals feedback for predicting rewards.

Multi-tasking What most people call multitasking is really task-switching. When it comes to attention and productivity, the human brain has a finite amount. With the exception of automatic behavior (like walking or chewing gum), the brain is forced to concentrate on just one thing at a time. Moving back and forth between several tasks actually wastes productivity, because our attention is expended on the act of switching gears—plus, we never get fully "in the zone" for either activity.

Myelination Myelin is a fatty sheath wrapped around nerve fibers. Through its special construction, myelin accelerates the propagation of impulses along nerve fibers. Myelin is an essential part of white matter. The main purpose of a myelin sheath is to increase the speed at which impulses propagate along the myelinated fiber. Along unmyelinated fibers, impulses move continuously as waves, but, in myelinated fibers, they "hop" or propagate by saltatory conduction.

Myelin Sheath The myelin sheath has two functions: insulation and acceleration of impulse conduction. Insulation is important for the prevention of short-circuits. When the myelin sheath is damaged or disappears, the conduction of impulses along nerve fibers slows down or fails completely. Consequently, brain functions become hampered or are lost.

N

Negative Punishment In operant conditioning, the theory of removing something pleasant to influence behavior. For instance, a teacher might "take away" a pleasant consequence (free reading time) from a student in order to discourage that student's maladaptive behavior (playing games on his phone during math class).

Negative Reinforcement In operant conditioning, the theory of removing something noxious to influence behavior. For instance, a teacher might "take away" an unpleasant consequence (detention) from a student's schedule in order to encourage that student's good behavior (studying hard for a test).

Neocortex (Brain Model)   Two large cerebral hemispheres that play a dominant role in human cognition. These hemispheres have been responsible for the development of language, abstract thought, imagination, and consciousness. Flexible and with infinite learning abilities, the neocortex has enabled the development of human culture.

Neural Networks   A fundamental unit of the nervous system. Without communication between neurons, no complex behavior or thought would exist.

Neurogenesis   Growth and development of neurons. This process is most active while a baby is developing in the womb and is responsible for the production of the brain's neurons. The development of new neurons continues during adulthood in two regions of the brain.

Neuron   Specialized cells in the brain and throughout the nervous system that conduct electrical impulses to, from, and within the brain. Neurons are composed of a main cell body, a single axon for outgoing electrical signals, and a varying number of dendrites for incoming signals in electrical form. There are up to 100 billion neurons in an average adult brain.

Neuroscience   A science whose objective is to understand consciousness or how a person arises out of a clump of squishy matter. This is a field where psychology meets biology. Because of powerful new tools at our disposal, including MEG, FMRI, computer simulations, and medical imaging, the field doubles the knowledge of brain and neuroscience every decade or so.

Neurotransmitter   Transmit signals across a chemical synapse from the firing neuron to a target neuron. Neurotransmitters are released into the synaptic cleft where they are received by receptors on other neurons. Neurotransmitters play a major role in shaping everyday life and functions. Their exact numbers are unknown but more than 100 chemical messengers have been identified.

Non-REM   Stages one through four of the sleep cycle. During these stages, scientists believe that this is where the restorative actions of sleep are taking place in the body. It is in these stages that all the things that we consider beneficial for a good night's sleep for our bodies take place.

Novelty in Attention   Something that is new, original, or unusual grabs our attention for long enough that we can redirect our subsequent attention onto the area of real interest.

Nucleus (cell) A double membrane-bound organelle that contains the genetic information of the cell. The nucleus acts like the brain of the cell. It helps control eating, movement, and reproduction.

O

Occipital Lobe The rearmost lobe in each cerebral hemisphere of the cerebral cortex of the brain. The occipital lobe is the visual processing center of the human brain.

Olfactory Bulb A neural structure of the vertebrate forebrain involved in the sense of smell.

Operant Conditioning E. L. Thorndike (1929) famously carried out experiments with cats using a puzzle box in which he demonstrated that if an action brings a reward, then that action becomes "stamped" into the mind. This became known as operant conditioning and lead to a field of study dealing with stimulus and response, which had a large impact on learning methods.

P

Parietal Lobe The upper back part of the skull houses the parietal lobe. This region also receives and processes sensory information that pertains to taste, temperature, and touch.

Perseverate Persistent repetition of the same activity.

Plasticity The adaptability of an organism to change in response to its environment. This is one of the primary attributes of learning and the brain that results in students gaining agency over their own learning.

Pons (Latin for "bridge"): Part of the brainstem, and lies between the midbrain (above) and the medulla oblongata (below), and in front of the cerebellum. This region of the brainstem includes neural pathways or tracts that conduct signals from the brain down to the cerebellum and medulla, and tracts that carry the sensory signals up into the thalamus.

Positive Punishment In operant conditioning, the theory of adding something noxious to influence behavior. For instance, a teacher might "add" an unpleasant consequence (detention) to a student's schedule in order to discourage that student's maladaptive behavior (playing games on his phone during math class).

Positive Reinforcement   In operant conditioning, the theory of adding something pleasant that makes the behavior more likely to reoccur. For instance, a teacher might "add" a pleasant consequence (cookie, star) to a student in order to encourage that student's good behavior.

Postsynaptic Terminal   The terminal at the receiving end of an axon that looks for the neurotransmitter that has been directed to the synaptic cleft between two communicating neurons.

Potential   As human beings, we have potential to be successful in life and to be happy. Factors that influence a person's potential are both genetic and environmental. We are born with a certain brain and immediately our surroundings play a part in who we are and who we become.

Prefrontal Cortex   Part of the brain located at the front of the frontal lobe. It is implicated in a variety of complex behaviors, including higher-order thinking like planning, predicting, synthesizing, and greatly contributes to personality development.

Presynaptic Terminal   The terminal at the transmission end of the axon of the firing neuron where electrical impulses are changed to chemical neurotransmitters and directed into the synaptic cleft between the two neurons.

Primacy Effect   Remembering the first thing in a list of items. A person can usually recall the first and last entry in a list of items; in psychology, described as "recency" and "primacy" effects.

Pruning   Reducing the number of neuronal synapses, axons, or dendrites in response to use or growth signals.

Pygmalion Effect   An effect described by Rosenthal & Jacobson (1968) in which teachers were told that certain children would be bloomers (based on IQ scores). Indeed, these children showed statistically significant gains favoring the experimental group of "intellectual bloomers." This led to the conclusion that teacher expectations, particularly for the youngest children, can influence student achievement.

R

Rapid Eye Movement   A jerky motion of a person's eyes occurring in REM sleep. During REM sleep, consolidation of the things we learned during the day is occurring. The brain processes information that was experienced during consciousness—both in terms of (i) consolidating memories that we want to keep, and (ii) getting rid of memories that we don't want to keep.

Recall (Memory)   Remembering—or subsequent re-accessing of events or information from the past, which have been previously encoded and stored in memory (in the brain). During recall, the brain "replays" a pattern of neural activity that was originally generated in response to a particular event, echoing the brain's perception of the real event.

Recency Effect   The most recent information is easiest to remember. One can usually recall the thing that was said last in a list of items.

Reinforcement   Anything that increases the likelihood that a response will occur. Reinforcement increases or strengthens behavior.

REM   See Rapid Eye Movement.

Repetition   The recurrence of an action or event. The action of repeating something that has already been said or written.

Reptilian Brain   The oldest part of the brain, which controls the body's vital functions such as heart rate, breathing, body temperature, and balance.

Resilience   The capacity to recover quickly from difficulties. The process of adapting well in the face of adversity, trauma, tragedy, threats, or even significant sources of stress. Resilience means "bouncing back" from difficult experiences.

Reticular Activating System (RAS)   A portal through which nearly all information enters the brain (smell is the exception—goes directly to the brain's emotional area).

Reward or Punishment Method   Way of learning by means of operant conditioning. The behavioral psychologist B. F. Skinner suggested that consequences for behavior (either reward or punishment) would bring about/reinforce learning.

Routine Expert   Mastering procedures in such a way as to become highly efficient and accurate (but not flexible or adaptable in situations that are outside the routine). People who are routine experts can accelerate efficiency through well-practiced routines.

Ruminate   Think deeply about something. When people ruminate, they overthink or obsess about situations or life events, such as work or relationships. Ruminating is like a record that's stuck and keeps repeating the same lyrics.

S

Saltatory Conduction   The action potential jumps from node to node in a process called saltatory conduction, which can increase conduction velocity up to ten times, without an increase in axonal diameter.

Self-regulation Enables individuals to set priorities and resist impulsive actions or responses. These skills are crucial for learning and development. Self-regulation skills allow children to filter distractions, prioritize tasks, set and achieve goals, and control impulses.

Sensory Input Information processing starts with input from the sensory organs (eyes, ears, hands, tongue, skin, nose etc.), which transform physical stimuli such as touch, heat, sound waves, or photons of light into electrochemical signals.

Serotonin A neurotransmitter that aids learning and memory formation. Serotonin enhances the neuron's electrical impulse, creating enduring memory. Serotonin is especially active in transmitting impulses between nerve cells, and contributing to wellbeing and happiness.

Sleep A condition of body and mind such as that which typically recurs for several hours every night, in which the nervous system is relatively inactive, the eyes closed, the postural muscles relaxed, and consciousness practically suspended.

Sleep Hygiene Healthy approach to sleep time that enables quality and quantity for the human mind and body to experience rejuvenation.

Spines (Dendritic) A small membranous protrusion from a neuron's dendrite that typically receives input from a single axon at the synapse. Dendritic spines serve as a storage site for synaptic strength and help transmit electrical signals to the neuron's cell body.

Stimulus Stimulus is something that causes a reaction, especially interest, excitement, or energy.

Stress A state of mental or emotional strain or tension resulting from adverse circumstances.

Switching An ability to move between mental tasks. Studies show that the brain is not able to multi-task, but instead the brain disengages from one task in order to engage in the next task.

Synapse A junction between two nerve cells, consisting of a minute gap across which impulses pass by diffusion of a neurotransmitter. Information from one neuron flows to another neuron across a synapse. The synapse contains a small gap separating neurons. The synapse consists of: i) a presynaptic ending that contains neurotransmitters mitochondria and other cell organelles; ii) a postsynaptic ending that contains receptor sites for neurotransmitters; and iii) a synaptic cleft or space between the presynaptic and postsynaptic endings.

Synaptic Cleft A microscopic space between neurons at a nerve synapse across which a nerve impulse is transmitted by a neurotransmitter.

Synesthesia   A neurological phenomenon in which stimulation of one sensory or cognitive pathway leads to automatic, involuntary experiences in a second sensory or cognitive pathway.

T

Talent   Innate ability, aptitude, or faculty; above average ability. Specifically a special ability that allows someone to do something well.

Temporal Lobe   In front of the occipital lobe, the temporal lobe is associated with auditory processing and olfaction. It is key to being able to understand meaningful speech, hearing, and selective listening—attributes that are vital to learning.

Thalamus   (Latin for "room") Processes sight, sound, touch, and taste, sorting the senses into the appropriate parts of the brain. Smell is the only sense that bypasses the thalamus and goes directly to the limbic system.

Threat Response   An emotional response to an actual or perceived environmental event. The limbic system is the large part of the brain that is permanently alert to threats and rewards. It tracks thought related to people, objects, and events. The limbic system includes the hippocampus, which is central to storing memories, and the amygdala, which is hypersensitive to threats or perceived threats.

Trait   A distinguishing quality or characteristic pertaining to a person's nature.

Transcranial Magnetic Stimulation   A noninvasive procedure that uses magnetic fields to stimulate nerve cells in the brain. This form of neuro stimulation can be used to cause electric current to flow in targeted regions of the brain via electromagnetic induction.

V

Vesicle   Neurotransmitters (brain chemicals) are packaged in tiny, bubble-like compartments known as vesicles, which are typically located at the end of one cell ready to cross the small gap (synaptic cleft) to communicate with another cell.

Visual Cortex   Located in the most posterior portion of the brain's occipital lobe, the visual cortex processes visual information by recognizing and locating objects. This is the pathway through which conscious visual perception takes place.

W

Wakefulness   Wakefulness is an arousal state that is opposite to sleeping. Activation of neurons that make the neurotransmitters norepinephrine, serotonin, and histamine is needed for waking.

Working Memory   Governs one's ability to retain and manipulate distinct pieces of information over short periods of time. Working memory can hold and manipulate information for use in the immediate future.

White Matter   The part of the brain that contains myelinated nerve fibers. The white matter is white because it is the color of myelin, the insulation covering the nerve fibers. Myelin acts as an insulator, increasing the speed of transmission of all nerve signals.

Wiring   No two people have the same brain, not even twins. Every brain is wired differently. What you do and learn in life physically changes what your brain looks like—it literally rewires it. When the human child is born, the brain begins to wire itself. Soon thereafter, weak unused, or wrong connections are pruned away and useful ones are strengthened. Brains are wired according to experiences.

References

1. Cunningham, S., D. O'Mahony, eds. *HDIL Reflections: How Do I Learn* (HDIL Summer Institute, K-2, HDIL Summer Institute Notes, Washington, DC, 2013).
2. Herbert, R. Opinion: Sharing the Pain. *The New York Times* (New York), 2008, chap. op-ed.
3. Wise, B. *Dropout Costs Priced for 50 Major US Cities* (Washington Alliance for Excellent Education, Washington, DC, 2009).
4. Ferner, M. The Full Cost of Incarceration in the US. *Huffington Post*, 2016.
5. Rowe, C. Is Test-Prep Teaching? It Takes Up 18 Percent of School Time. *The Seattle Times* (Seattle, WA), 2014.
6. NAEP. *Nation's Report Card* (National Association of Educational Performance, 2019). https://www.nationsreportcard.gov/highlights/reading/2019/.
7. NAEP. *Scores Have Flat Lined for 30 Years* (National Association of Educational Performance, Associated Press, New York, 2019).
8. Zegers, K. By the Numbers: School Shootings Since Columbine. *US & World News*, 2019.
9. Hammond, B. *The Oregonian* (Oregonian, Oregon Live), 2019. https://www.ore gonlive.com/crime/2019/12/judge-revokes-federal-grazing-permit-for-ham mond-ranches-inc.html.
10. Murphy, S., G. McKenna, P. Downes. *Education Gaps and Future Solutions* (Dublin City University Institute of Education, Educational Disadvantage Center, Dublin, Ireland, 2019).
11. Santhanam, L. *Youth Suicide Rates Are on the Rise in the U.S.*, 2019. https://www.pbs.org/newshour/health/youth-suicide-rates-are-on-the-rise-in-the-u-s.
12. Lindsey, M. A., A. H. Sheftall, Y. Xiao, S. Joe. Trends of Suicidal Behaviors Among High School Students in the United States: 1991–2017. *Pediatrics* **144**, 1–10 (2019).
13. Carnavale, A. *In This Together: Foreword* (Georgetown University Center on Education and the Workforce, Washington, DC, 2014).
14. Carnevale, P., A. R. Hanson, A. Gulish. *Failure to Launch: Structural Shift and the New Lost Generation* (Georgetown Public Policy Institute, Georgetown University, Washington, DC, 2013).
15. Dweck, C. S. *Mindset: The New Psychology of Success* (Random House, New York, 2006).
16. Hatano, G., Y. Osuro, Commentary: Re-Conceptualizing School Learning Using Insight from Expertise Research. *Educational Researcher* **32**, 26–29 (2003).
17. Pink, D. *Drive* (Riverhead Books, New York, 2009).

18. Bransford, J. D. *et al. The Second International Handbook of Educational Change*, A. Hargreaves, M. Fullan, D. Hopkins, A. Leiberman, eds. (Springer, Dordrecht, The Netherlands, 2010), pp. 825–856.

19. Coulson, A. J. *New NAEP Scores Extend Dismal Trend in US Education Productivity: CATO at Liberty* (CATO Institute, Washington, DC, 2013).

20. Feldman, D., A. Smith, B. Waxman. *Why We Drop Out: Understanding and Disrupting Student Pathways to Leaving School* (Teachers College Press, Columbia University, New York, 2017).

21. Barbaro, M., D. Goldstein. The Daily on NPR. *New York Times* (National Public Radio), 2019.

22. National Science Foundation. *Women, Minorities and Persons with Disabilities in Science and Engineering* (NSF, Arlington, VA, 2009).

23. Reardon, S. F. *Whither Opportunity? Rising Inequality, Schools and Children's Life Chances*, R. Murnane, G. Duncan, eds. (Russell Sage Foundation, New York, 2011).

24. Boorstin, D. J. *The Discoverers: A History of Man's Search to Know His World and Himself* (Random House Inc., New York, 1985).

25. Skinner, B. F. *Contingencies of Reinforcement: A Theoretical Analysis.* Century Psychology Series (Meredith Corporation, New York, 1969).

26. Chomsky, N. Review of B. F. Skinner, Verbal Behavior. *Language* **35**, 26–58 (1959).

27. Kaplan, A. *The Conduct of Inquiry: Methodology for Behavioral Science* (Chandler Publishing Company, San Francisco, CA, 1964).

28. Kahneman, D., P. Slovic, A. Tversky. Judgment Under Uncertainty: Heuristics and Biases. *Science* **185** (1982).

29. Gazzaniga, M. S. *The Consciousness Instinct* (Farrar, Straus and Giroux, New York, 2018).

30. Sobel, D. Skinner Is Dead. *New York Times* (New York), 1990.

31. Graesser, A. C. Emotions During the Learning of Difficult Material. *The Psychology of Learning and Motivation* **57**, 183–225 (2012).

32. Cho, R. W. *et al.* Phosphorylation of Complexin by PKA Regulates Activity-Dependent Spontaneous Neurotransmitter Release and Structural Synaptic Plasticity. *Neuron* **88**, 749–761 (2015).

33. Panksepp, J. *Affective Neuroscience: The Foundations of Human and Animal Emotions* (Oxford University Press, New York, 1989).

34. Rosenthal, R., L. Jacobson. *Pygmalion in the Classroom* (Holt Rinehard and Winson, New York, 1968).

35. Thorndike, E. L. Animal intelligence: An Experimental Study of the Associate Processes in Animals. *Psychological Review: Monograph Supplement* **2**, 1–8 (1898).

36. Thorndike, E. L., R. S. Woodworth. The Influence of Improvement in one Mental Function Upon the Efficiency of Other Functions. *Psychological Review* **8**, 247–261 (1901).

37. Perry, B. *The Boy Who Was Raised as a Dog: What Traumatized Children Can Teach Us About Loss, Love and Healing* (Basic Books, New York, 2006).

38. Ebbinghaus, H. *Über das Gedächtnis (Memory: A Contribution to Experimental Psychology)* (Teachers College, Columbia University, New York, 1885/1913).

39. O'Mahony, T. K., E. Thompson, R. Carr. *Brain-Centric Design Transforms a Learning Community Immediately and Forever.* Paper presented at the International Conference on E-Learning in the Workplace, Columbia University Teachers College, New York, 2019.

40. Du Sautoy, M. Rebooting Britain: Teach Kids to See in Four Dimensions. *Wired UK Magazine*, 2009.

41. Pinker, S. *The Blank Slate: The Modern Denial of Human Nature* (Viking, New York, 2002).

42. Caron, C. In 19 States, It's Still Legal to Spank Children in Public Schools. *The New York Times*, 2018.

43. Texas Education Code. *Title 2*, 2013, Section 37.0011. https://texas.public.law/statutes/tex._educ._code_section_37.0011.

44. Gershoff, E. T., S. A. Font. Corporal Punishment in U.S. Public Schools: Prevalence, Disparities in Use, and Status in State and Federal Policy. *Social Policy Report* **30**, no. 1 (2016) (PubMed Central National Institutes of Health).

45. Baylis, E. *et al. Pushed Out: Youth Voices on the Dropout Crisis in Philadelphia.* Participatory Action Research Report (Project U-Turn, Youth United for Change, Philadelphia, 2011).

46. Felitti, V. J. *et al.* Relationship of Childhood Abuse and Household Dysfunction to Many of the Leading Causes of Death in Adults: The Adverse Childhood Experiences (ACE) Study. *American Journal of Preventive Medicine: Elsevier* **14**, 245–258 (1998).

47. Brown, T. T., A. J. Daly. Editorial: Welcome to Educational Neuroscience. *Educational Neuroscience. Sage* **1**, 1–2 (2016).

48. Schlinger, H. D. Not so Fast, Mr. Pinker: A Behaviorist Looks at the Blank Slate. A Review of Steven Pinker's the Blank Slate: The Modern Denial of Human Nature. *Behavior and Social Issues* **12**, 75–79 (2002).

49. HHS. *Policy Statement on Expulsion and Suspension Policies in Early Childhood Settings* (US Department of Health and Human Services, US Deptartment of Education, 2016). https://challengingbehavior.cbcs.usf.edu/docs/policy-statement-ece-expulsions-suspensions.pdf.

50. Balfanz, R., B. Vaughan, J. Fox. Sent Home and Put Off-Track: The Antecedents, Disproportionalities, and Consequences of Being Suspended in the Ninth Grade. *Journal of Applied Resesrch on Children* **5**, Article 13 (2014).

51. Bracey, G. The Sixteenth Bracey Report on the Condition of Public Education. *Phi Delta Kappan Magazine,* 2006.

52. Donati, L. *Learning and the Brain* (Institute for Connecting Neuroscience with Teaching and Learning, Neural Education 2.1, Washington, DC, 2020), p. 24.

53. Hublin, J. *et al.* Initial Upper Palaeolithic Homo Sapiens from Bacho Kiro Cave, Bulgaria. *Nature* **581** (2020).

54. Despain, D. Early Humans Used Brain-Power, Innovation and Teamwork to Dominate the Planet. *Scientific American*, 2010.

55. Smithsonian Science. Bigger Brains: Complex Brains for a Complex World. *Smithsonian*, 2019.

56. Bransford, J. D., A. L. Brown, R. Cocking. *How People Learn: Brain, Mind, Experience and School* (National Academy Press, Washington, DC, 2000).

57. Trezza, V., P. J. J. Baarendse, L. J. M. J. Vanderschuren. The Pleasures of Play: Pharmacological Insights into Social Reward Mechanisms. *Trends in Pharmacological Sciences* **31** (2010).

58. Lortie, D. *Schoolteacher* (University of Chicago Press, Chicago, 1975).

59. Latham, J. Payment by Results Revisited? *History Today* **41** (1991).

60. Wilson, E. O. *Consilience: The Unity of Knowledge* (Alfred A. Knopf, Inc., New York, 1998).

61. V. Strauss, Bill and Melinda Gates Have Spent Billions to Shape Education Policy: Now, They Say, They're 'Skeptical' of 'Billionaires' Trying to Do Just That. *Washington Post*, 2020.

62. Goleman, D. *Working with Emotional Intelligence* (Bantam Books, New York, 1998).

63. Baddeley, A. D. *Working Memory* (Oxford University Press, New York, 1986).

64. Miller, G. A. The Magical Number Seven, Plus or Minus Two: Some Limits on Our Capacity for Processing Information. *Psychological Review* **63**, 81–97 (1956).

65. Baddeley, A. The Magical Number Seven: Still Magic After All These Years? *Psychological Review* **10**, 353–356 (1994).

66. Smith, S. *The Smith Lab* (PhD Program, Molecular and Cellular Physiology, Stanford, 2019).

67. Kearsley, G. *Explorations in Learning & Instruction: The Theory Into Practice Database*, 2010. https://library.upei.ca/explorations.

68. Cowan, N. The Magical Number 4 in Short-Term Memory: A Reconsideration of Mental Storage Capacity. *Behavioral and Brain Sciences* **24**, 87–114 (2001).

69. O'Mahony, T. K. *et al. Edulearn 17: Neuroscience Foundations—9th Annual International Conference on Education and New Learning Technologies* (Open Education Europe, Barcelona, Spain, 2017).

70. Boyce, W. T., B. J. Ellis. Biological Sensitivity to Context: An Evolutionary-Developmental Theory of the Origins and Functions of Stress Reactivity. *Developmental Psychopathology* **17**, 271–301 (2005).

71. Boyce, W. T. *The Orchid and the Dandelion: Why Some Children Struggle and How All Can Thrive* (Knopf Doubleday Publishing Group, New York, 2018).

72. Shonkoff, J. P., W. T. Boyce, B. S. McEwen. Neuroscience, Molecular Biology, and the Childhood Roots of Health Disparities: Building a New Framework for Health Promotion and Disease Prevention. *JAMA, the Journal of the American Medical Association* **301**, 2252–2259 (2009).

73. Moaveni, A. 'It Could Have Been Me': On the Trail of the British Teenagers Who Became 'Brides of Isis'. *The Guardian Life Style*, 2019.

74. Vaill, P. B. *Learning as a Way of Being: Strategies for Survival in a World of Permanent White Water* (Jossey Bass, San Francisco, CA, 1996).

75. Shatz, C. The Developing Brain. *Scientific American* **267**, 60–67 (1992).

76. Chomsky, N. Three Models for the Description of Language. *IRE Transactions on Information Theory* **2**, 113–124 (1956).

77. Ericsson, K. A., J. Smith. *Toward a General Theory of Expertise: Prospects and Limits* (Cambridge University Press, Cambridge, MA, 1991).

78. Brown, R. E. The Life and Work of Donald Olding Hebb, Canada's Greatest Psychologist. *Proceedings of the Nova Scotia Institute of Science* **44**, 1–25 (2007).

79. Hebb, D. *The Organization of Behavior* (Wiley & Sons, New York, 1949).

80. Miller, G. A. The Cognitive Revolution: A Historical Perspective. *Trends in Cognitive Science* **7** (2003).

81. Doidge, N. *The Brain That Changes Itself* (Penguin, London, 2007).

82. Diamond, M. Dr. Diamond's Biography. *History of Neuroscience* **7** (2012).

83. Linden, D. *The Accidental Mind: How Brain Evolution Has Given Us Love, Memory, Dreams, and God* (Harvard University Press, Boston, MA, 2007).

84. Willis, J. *Research-Based Strategies to Ignite Student Learning: Insights from a Neurologist and Classroom Teacher* (Association for Supervision and Curriculum Development, Alexandria, VA, 2006).

85. O'Mahony, T. K. *Geography and Education: Through the Souls of Our Feet* (Educare Press, Seattle, WA, 2002), 2nd ed., p. 250.

86. Bliss, T. V., T. Lomo, Long-Lasting Potentiation of Synaptic Transmission in the Dentate Area of the Anaesthetized Rabbit Following Stimulation of the Perforant Path. *Journal of Physiology* **232**, 331–356 (1973).

87. Lemorick, M. D. *Time* (Time Life, New York, 1999), vol. 154.

88. Willis, J. How to Teach Students About the Brain. *Educational Leadership* **67** (2009).

89. del Prado Martin, F. M. *New Measures of Human Brain Processing Speed*. MIT Technology Review, Emerging Technology from the arXiv, 2009. https://www.technologyreview.com/2009/08/25/210267/new-measure-of-human-brain-processing-speed/.

90. Kandel, E., J. Schwartz, T. Jessell, S. Siegelbaum, A. Hudsprth. *Principles of Neural Science* (The MacGraw-Hill Companies, New York, 2013), 5th ed.

91. Widmann, M. *Institute for Connecting Neuroscience with Teaching and Learning* (Neural Education, Washington, DC, 2019).

92. Bereiter, C., M. Scardamalia. *Surpassing Ourselves: An Inquiry into the Nature and Implications of Expertise* (Open Court Publishing Company, Chicago, 1993), p. 279.

93. Atman, R. S. *et al.* Engineering Design Processes: A Comparison of Students and Expert Practioners. *Journal of Engineering Education* **96**, 359–379 (2007).

94. Callahan, R. E. *Education and the Cult of Efficiency* (University of Chicago Press, Chicago, 1962).

95. Ford, H. *My Life and Work*, S. Crowther, ed. (Doubleday, Page & Co, New York, 1922).

96. Cubberley, E. P. *Public School Administration: A Statement of the Fundamental Principles Underlying the Organization and Administration of Public Education* (Houghton Mifflin, New York, 1916).

97. Bransford, J. D. Preparing People for Rapidly Changing Environments. *Journal of Engineering Education* **96** (2007).

98. Rogoff, B., R. Paradise, R. Mejia-Arauz, M. Correa-Chavez, C. Angelillo. First Hand Learning Through Intent Participation. *Annual Review of Psychology* **54**, 175–203 (2003).

99. Berliner, D. Our Impoverished View of Education Reform. *Teachers College Record* **108** (2012).

100. Dweck, C. S., E. L. Leggett. A Social-Cognitive Approach to Motivation and Personality *Psychological Review* **95**, 256–273 (1988).

101. Trummert, W. *Effects of a Collaborative RTI Based Integrated Kindergarten Motor and Academic Program* (University of Puget Sound, Olympia, Tacoma, WA, 2016).

102. Smith, S. W. Individualized Education Programs (IEPs) in Special Education—From Intent to Acquiescence. *Exceptional Children* **57**, 6–14 (1990).

103. Trummert, W. *Institue for Connecting Neuroscience with Teaching and Learning*, Kieran O'Mahony, ed. (Neural Education, Seattle, WA, 2019).

104. Beck, C. *Four-Leaf Clover for Bilateral Coordination*, 2020. OT Toolbox dot com, www.theottoolbox.com/.

105. Bunge, S. *Structural Connectivity Sets the Stage for Later Reasoning Ability* (The DANA Foundation Study, Building Blocks of Cognition Laboratory, Berkeley, CA, 2017).

106. Palmer, A. These two brains both belong to three-year-olds, so why is one so much bigger? *Telegraph* (Telegraph Media Group, London, 2012).

107. Brown, S. L., C. C. Vaughan. *Play: How It Shapes the Brain, Opens the Imagination and Invigorates the Soul* (Avery, New York, 2009).

108. Woody, A., E. D. Hooker, P. M. Zoccola, S. S. Dickerson. Social-Evaluative Threat, Cognitive Load, and the Cortisol and Cardiovascular Stress Response. *Psychoneuroendocrinology* **97**, 149–155 (2018).

109. Lockett, P. To Curb the Teacher Shortage, We Need to Think Bigger About the Problem. *Forbes Magazine Online*, 2019.

110. Russakoff, D. *The Prize: Whose in Charge of America's Schools* (Houghton Mifflin Harcourt Publishing, New York, 2015).

111. Innovate America: National Innovation Initiate Report. *Thriving in a World of Challenge and Change*, 2004. https://www.compete.org/programs/previous-work/2728-national-innovation-initiative.

112. Ziaian-Ghafari, N., D. H. Berg. Compassion Fatigue: The Experiences of Teachers Working with Students with Exceptionalities. *Exceptionality Education International* **29**, 32–53 (2019).

113. O'Mahony T. K. *et al. EduLearn 17: 9th Annual International Conference on Education and New Learning Technologies* (IATED, Open Education Europe, Barcelona, Spain, 2017).

114. Miller, G. A., E. Walker. *Cognitive Science* (The Alfred P. Sloan Foundation, Rochester, NY, 1978).

115. Sabelli, N. Complexity, Technology, Science, and Education. *The Journal of the Learning Sciences* **15**, 5–10 (2006).

116. Gurrola, C., K. O'Mahony, eds. *Oversight Committee Meeting for NSF Funded Project in Advanced Materials* (CAM, Seattle, WA, 2008).

117. Sweller, J. Cognitive Load During Problem Solving: Effects on Learning. *Cognitive Science* **12**, 257–285 (1988).

118. Rothwell, J. The Declining Productivity of Education. *Social Mobility Memos*, 2016. https://www.brookings.edu/blog/social-mobility-memos/2016/12/23/the-declining-productivity-of-education/.

119. National Science Board. *"Science and Engineering Indicators": High School and Graduation Rates in the United States and Other OECD Nations* (National Science Foundation, Arlington, VA, 2012).

120. Maslow, A. H. *Motivation and Personality* (Harper & Row, New York, 1970).

121. Darling-Hammmond, L. Building a Belonging Classroom. *Edutopia: Classroom Management* (2019). https://www.edutopia.org/video/building-belonging-classroom.

122. Berninger, V. W., T. L. Richards. *Brain Literacy for Educators and Psychologists* (Academic Press, New York, 2002).

123. Davidson, R. J., B. S. McEwen. Social Influences on Neuroplasticity: Stress and Interventions to Promote Well-Being. *Nature Neuroscience* (2012). Doi:10.1038/nn.3093.

124. Grandmother, V., D. O'Mahony, eds. *Institue for Connecting Neuroscience with Teaching and Learning* (Neural Education, Seattle, WA, 2019).

125. Perry, B. *Children, Youth and Violence: The Search for Solutions*, J. Osofsky, ed. (Guilford Press, New York, 1997), pp. 124–148.

126. Diamond, M. *Enriching Heredity: The Impact of the Environment on the Anatomy of the Brain* (New York Free Press, New York, 1988).

127. Hammond, Z. *Culturally Responsive Teaching and the Brain: Promoting Authentic Engagement and Rigor Among Culturally and Linguistically Diverse Students* (Corwin, Thousand Oaks, CA, 2015).

128. Trevena, J., H. Smith. Handcuffed 5-Year-Old Sparks Suit. *CBS News: The Early Show*, 2005.

129. Powell, A. How Sputnik Changed U.S. Education: Fifty Years Later, Panelists Consider a New Science Education 'Surge'. *The Harvard Gazette*, 2007.

130. National Commission on Excellence in Education. *A Nation at Risk: The Imperative for Educaitonal Reform* (US Department of Education, Washington, DC, 1983).

131. Sophocles. *Seven Tragedies of Sophocles: Antigone* (University of Cantebury, Christchurch, 2014), Sophocles' Antigone by Robin Bond (trans.) Is Licensed Under a Creative Commons Attribution 4.0 International License.

132. Heyman, J., D. Ariely. Effort for Payment: A Tale of Two Markets. *Psychological Science: American Psychological Society* **15**, 787–793 (2004).

133. Piaget, J. *Piaget Rediscovered*, E. R. Ripple, V. N. Rockcastle, eds. (Cornell University Press, New York, 1964).

134. Teachers in Action. *Singularity Event in Schools*, T. K. O'Mahony, ed. (Institute for Connecting Neuroscience with Teaching and Learning, Seattle, WA, 2020), pp. 1–3.

135. Munsey, C. The Kids Aren't All Right: New Data from APA's Stress in America Survey Indicate Parents Don't Know What's Bothering Their Children. *Monitor on Psychology* **41** (2010).

136. Fair, D. A. The Big Reveal: Precision Mapping Shines a Gigantic Floodlight on the Cerebellum. *Neuron: Elsevier* **100**, 773–776 (2018).

137. Hinton, G. *Artificial Intelligence* (YouTube, University of Toronto, Toronto, 2018).

Index